Some Account of the Pennsylvania Hospital

PUBLICATIONS OF THE INSTITUTE OF THE HISTORY
OF MEDICINE

FOURTH   SERIES
Bibliotheca Medica Americana
VOLUME   VI

BENJAMIN FRANKLIN

SOME ACCOUNT OF THE

PENNSYLVANIA

HOSPITAL

Printed in Facsimile, with an Introduction by

I. BERNARD COHEN

BALTIMORE:

THE JOHNS HOPKINS PRESS

To JOHN & LUCIA FULTON

PREFACE

FRANKLIN'S book on the Pennsylvania Hospital has been out of print for almost a century and a half and has been neglected by students of the history of medicine and American literature. It is here reproduced in facsimile from the copy in the De Golyer Collection of the History of Science, Library of the University of Oklahoma. That collection, being built up by Dr. E. De Golyer, is one of the youngest great collections of books in the history of science, just as Oklahoma is one of the youngest states (1907) in the Union; Franklin was a firm believer in the westward destiny of America and the first American to exemplify that belief in public action or policy.

I acknowledge the kindness of Dr. Edward B. Krumbhaar, who supplied information and copies of his own writings on the history of the Pennsylvania Hospital and on medicine in eighteenth-century Pennsylvania. Finally, I record my thanks to the Boston Athenaeum, and especially to the librarian, Mr. Walter Muir Whitehill, for making available to me for study a copy of Franklin's book which is one of their prized possessions.

February, 1954   I. B. C.

INTRODUCTION

I. BERNARD COHEN

*Human felicity is produced not so much by
great pieces of fortune that seldom happen as
by little advantages that occur every day.*
— *B. Franklin*

TWO HUNDRED years ago Franklin published his book
about the Pennsylvania Hospital which is reproduced in
facsimile in the present edition. This interesting book has
not been reprinted since 1817, nor has it appeared in any of the
editions of Franklin's writings.[1] Although listed in the standard
bibliography of Franklin's writings,[2] neither historians of medicine nor historians of American literature have paid it the attention it deserves.

From the typographical point of view, the original edition
is a splendid example of the good printing done by Benjamin
Franklin. For this reason, the original has been reproduced in
facsimile. Since Franklin's *Account of the Pennsylvania Hospital*
was not a record, but a part of his program to gain support for
America's first permanent hospital,[3] every device of style, docu-

---

[1] The most recent is Albert H. Smyth (editor): *The Writings of Benjamin
Franklin* (10 vols.; New York: The Macmillan Co., 1910).

[2] Paul Leicester Ford: *Franklin Bibliography:* A list of books written by, or
relating to, Benjamin Franklin (Brooklyn, N. Y.: [privately printed], 1889).
The book on the Pennsylvania Hospital is listed on p. 51 as No. 99.

[3] Some claim has been made that the Philadelphia General Hospital might
antedate the Pennsylvania Hospital. This question is answered in Francis R.
Packard's *Some Account of the Pennsylvania Hospital from its first Rise to the
Beginning of the Year 1938* (Philadelphia: Engle Press [for the Pennsylvania
Hospital], 1938), a title taken from Franklin's book of 1754.

mentation, and format was employed to engage the reader's attention, to hold his interest, and to elicit his sympathetic action. On the last page a form was provided for the reader to make his contribution, a modern device, shrewdly calculated to make the giving of charity easier.

Benjamin Franklin's activities in promoting institutions for the betterment of the daily lives of his fellow men are well known. Readers are aware of his initiative in proposing or supporting America's first circulating or subscription library, the school or academy that has grown into the University of Pennsylvania, a fire company, an insurance company, and a regular constabulary, and the introducing of paved, swept, and well-lit streets in Philadelphia.[4]

All too often, Franklin is presented as a "doer of good" for the community without indication of the influences both in Boston and Philadelphia that helped to condition his outlook on man and his needs. In his "Autobiography," Franklin told of two books, "which perhaps gave me a turn of thinking that had an influence on some of the principal future events of my life." These were "a book of Defoe's, called an Essay on Projects, and another of Dr. Mather's, called Essays to do Good."[5] Writing from France at the age of seventy-eight, he expressed his indebtedness to Cotton Mather. In a letter to Cotton's son Samuel,[6] Franklin wrote that as a boy, he had

[4] For Franklin's career, see Carl Van Doren: *Benjamin Franklin* (New York: The Viking Press, 1938); Paul Leicester Ford: *The Many-Sided Franklin* (New York: The Century Co., 1899).

[5] Cf. *The Works of Daniel Defoe*, with a memoir of his life and writings, by William Hazlitt (London: John Clements, 1843), vol. 3: *Essays upon Several Projects: or, Effectual Ways for Advancing the Interests of the Nation* . . . .

[6] Smyth, vol. 9, p. 208. Franklin to Samuel Mather: Passy, May 12, 1784.

found a copy of Mather's "Essays to do Good."[7] "It had been so little regarded by a former possessor, that several leaves of it were torn out; but the remainder gave me such a turn of thinking, as to have an influence on my conduct through life; for I have always set a greater value on the character of a *doer of good*, than on any other kind of reputation; and if I have been, as you seem to think, a useful citizen, the public owes the advantage of it to that book."

Those who think of Cotton Mather as the "typical" Puritan bigot may hold it odd that he had any influence on the liberal Franklin. Cotton Mather, however, has been a neglected figure in our history, and his full stature and character are not generally known. One revaluation of Mather, in recent years, has come from the study[8] of his interest in science.[9] It has been

---

[7] Cf. Thomas James Holmes: *Cotton Mather: A Bibliography of his Works* (Cambridge: Harvard University Press, 1940), vol. 1, pp. 89-95: *Bonifacius: An Essay upon the Good, that is to be devised and designed by those who desire to answer the great end of life, and to do good while they live . . . .* Franklin's youthful satires, directed against the Mathers, were signed "Silence Dogood." Franklin, according to Perry Miller, had "with diabolical cunning" taken "unto himself the cognomen of Silence (since Cotton Mather was possessed, according to the *Courant*, of an irresistable itch for scribbling) Dogood, a blasphemy for which he did penance in his old age" by writing the letter to Samuel Mather about the influence of Cotton's *Essays to Do Good* on his conduct through life. *From Colony to Province* (ref. 11, below), p. 410.

[8] A new perspective on Mather's scientific interests resulted from three papers by George Lyman Kittredge: "Cotton Mather's Election into the Royal Society," *Colonial Society of Massachusetts, Publications*, vol. 14 (1913), pp. 81-114; "Further Notes on Cotton Mather and the Royal Society," *ibid.*, 281-292; "Some Lost Works of Cotton Mather," *Massachusetts Historical Society, Proceedings*, vol. 45 (1911-12), pp. 418-479; "Cotton Mather's Scientific Communications to the Royal Society," *American Antiquarian Society, Proceedings*, vol. 26 (1916), pp. 18-57.

[9] Cf. Theodore Hornberger's essay on Mather's science in Thomas James Holmes: *Cotton Mather* (ref. 6, above), vol. 1, pp. 133-137.

shown that he was the author of the first account of spontaneous hybridization in plants.[10] Although his sponsorship of inoculation against the smallpox in 1721 has become part of the literature on colonial American medicine,[11] his manuscript treatise on medicine, *The Angel of Bethesda*, has only recently become subject to competent analysis.[12] Franklin's brother James carried on a running opposition to the Mathers in his *New England Courant* while Benjamin was still an apprentice, and the Franklins marshalled all possible evidence and argument, largely supplied by Dr. William Douglass, against inoculation as part of the anti-Mather campaign. But in later years Franklin became one of the chief advocates of inoculation in colonial America.[13]

[10] Cf. Conway Zirkle: *The Beginnings of Plant Hybridization* (Philadelphia: University of Pennsylvania Press, 1935), pp. 103-107; "Gregor Mendel & his Precursors," *Isis*, vol. 42 (1951), pp. 97-104 (esp. p. 98).

[11] Cf. Increase Mather: *Several Reasons proving that Inoculating or Transplanting the Small Pox is a Lawful Practice, and that it has been Blessed by God for the Saving of many a Life*; Cotton Mather: *Sentiments on the Small Pox Inoculated*; reprinted from the original folio sheet printed at Boston in 1721, with an introduction by George Lyman Kittredge (Cleveland: [printed for private distribution], 1921). The medical aspects of the subject are reviewed by Reginald H. Fitz: "Zabdiel Boylston, Inoculator, and the Epidemic of Smallpox in Boston in 1721," *Johns Hopkins Hospital Bulletin*, vol. 22 (1911), pp. 315 ff. For a fresh view of the whole subject, see Perry Miller: *The New England Mind: From Colony to Province* (Cambridge: Harvard University Press, 1953), ch. xxi: "The judgment of the smallpox."

[12] A general study of Mather's medicine, by Otho T. Beall, Jr. and Richard H. Shryock, will be published in the *Transactions* of the American Antiquarian Society. This work, which interprets the nature of Mather's medical thought and contributions, will include as an appendix some of the more significant chapters from his "Angel of Bethesda" (1725).

[13] Franklin's pamphlet recommending inoculation to Americans is reprinted, with an explanatory introduction, in I. Bernard Cohen: *Benjamin Franklin:*

SOME ACCOUNT OF THE PENNSYLVANIA HOSPITAL

Franklin quickly forgot the old hostility to the Mathers, once he had moved to Philadelphia. In 1724, on his first return trip to Boston, Franklin had a friendly visit with Cotton Mather, who received him in his library. On the way out, Mather turned suddenly to Franklin and said, *"Stoop, stoop!"* Franklin "did not understand him, till I felt my head hit against the [low] beam [which crossed the narrow passage]. He was a man that never missed any occasion of giving instruction, and upon this he said to me, '*You are young, and have the world before you; stoop as you go through it, and you will miss many hard thumps.*' This advice, thus beat into my head, has frequently been of use to me; and I often think of it, when I see pride mortified, and misfortunes brought upon people by their carrying their heads too high."

What could Franklin possibly have learned from Cotton Mather? At least a love of science. Loving science implied, in Mather's terms, a respect for nature, a recognition that the empirical evidence of the operations of nature in the external world are in perfect harmony with the principles of revelation and true faith. "Be sure," wrote Mather in his instructions to young ministers, "the Experimental Philosophy is that, in which alone your mind can be at all established."[14] The guide in this "experimental philosophy" was "the incomparable Sir Isaac Newton," acknowledged by Mather to be "the Perpetual

---

His Contribution to the American Tradition (Indianapolis: The Bobbs-Merrill Co., 1953), pp. 189-199.

[14] *Manuductio ad Ministerium: Directions for a Candidate of the Ministry* (Columbia University Press [for the Facsimile Text Society], 1938; a reprint of the original edition of 1726); cf. T. J. Holmes: *Cotton Mather* (ref. 6, above), vol. 2, pp. 617-636.

Dictator of the Learned World in the Principles of Natural Philosophy."[15]

Franklin, of course, had little sympathy with Cotton Mather's theological outpourings. Yet in Mather's activities in "that realm of social experience"[16] called by Max Weber "the Protestant ethic," we may catch a glimpse of Franklin in the making. Mather told his congregation to attend to "some settled business, wherein a Christian should for the most part spend most of his time and this, that so he may glorify God by doing of *Good* for *others*, and getting of *Good* for himself." Puritans in the Boston of Franklin's youth agreed that all the affairs of man are governed by the divine providence; thus the gaining of an estate is the result of divine favor. Initiative and industry are, of course, the necessary conditions for accumulating the world's goods, but they are not sufficient. In 1748, Franklin echoed the sentiments of his Puritan masters in his "Advice to a Young Tradesman." The "way to wealth," he wrote, "depends chiefly on two words, *industry* and *frugality*," but industry and frugality will be of avail only "if that Being who governs the world, to whom all should look for a blessing on their honest endeavours, doth not, in His wise providence, otherwise determine."[17]

"Honor the Lord with thy substance," Cotton Mather preached; "so shall thy barns be filled with plenty." Charitable

[15] Perry Miller: *From Colony to Province* (ref. 11, above) has shown that Mather referred to Newton as "our perpetual dictator" earlier than the *Manuductio:* the first use of this phrase by Mather was in a "spiritualizing tract" published in 1712, entitled *Thoughts for the Day of Rain.*

[16] Cf. Perry Miller: *From Colony to Province* (ref. 11, above), ch. xxiv: "Do-good"; *The New England Mind: The Seventeenth Century* (New York: The Macmillan Co., 1939), ch. xiv: "The social covenant."

[17] Smyth, vol. 2, pp. 370 ff.

men are esteemed by God, who rewards them "with remarkable success in their affairs, and increase of their property." Virtue, charity, and hard work in a "calling" procure divine favor and, therefore, an accumulation of the world's goods. But the man with an estate must remember that he is a "steward" and he must, therefore, as Cotton Mather put it, glorify God by contributing "unto the welfare of mankind, and such a relief of their miseries as may give the children of men better opportunity to glorify Him."

Mather's *Essays to do Good* contained the description of "the ravishing satisfaction" which a man "might find in relieving the distresses of a poor, mean, miserable neighbour." Readers were exhorted to do "service for the kingdom of our great Saviour in the world; or any thing to redress the miseries under which mankind is generally languishing." Poor Richard later put it in this way: "Serving God is doing good to man, but praying is thought an easier service, and therefore more generally chosen." On another occasion, Poor Richard said, "The noblest question in the world is, what good may I do in it?" This was merely an improved way of saying what Mather had already written down in the *Essays:* "Assume and assert the liberty of now and then thinking on the noblest question in the world: What good may I do in the world?"

Franklin's Junto, a private society for the mutual improvement of the members, and a focal point for the introduction of many useful institutions and reforms in Philadelphia, also showed Mather's influence. James Parton was one of the first historians who appreciated that Mather's "Neighborhood Benefit Societies" were the prototype of the Junto and that Mather's "Points of Consideration" (to be read at every meeting) are

[xv]

remarkably similar to the questions asked at the meetings of Franklin's Junto.[18]

Philadelphia, when Franklin arrived there in 1723, was characterized by a spirit of liberal tolerance that seems in marked contrast to theocratic Boston. But however far apart Calvinism and Quakerism might be on doctrinal or theological issues, they shared in common "the Protestant ethic." Franklin, therefore, probably found in Philadelphia a more familiar outlook on social goals and the rewards of virtuous conduct than we might otherwise have supposed. Puritan Boston, in other words, prepared him for his life in Philadelphia. Philadelphia and Benjamin Franklin made an ideal combination and both grew together— Franklin to become the foremost citizen of the New World, and Philadelphia to become the third largest city (not including those of India) in the eighteenth-century British Empire.[19] So similar were the precepts common in Quaker Philadelphia and Puritan Boston that both were put into the mouth of Poor Richard and what came out sounded just like Benjamin Franklin. "Diligence is a 'virtue' useful and laudable among men . . . . First, it is the Way to Wealth . . . . Frugality is a virtue too, and not of little use in life, the better Way to be Rich, for it has less toil and temptation. It is proverbial, *A penny saved is a penny got* . . . . "[20] These lines, excerpted from an essay on economic virtues written by William Penn, might have been written by

[18] James Parton: *Life and Times of Benjamin Franklin* (New York: Mason Brothers, 1864), vol. 1, pp. 47-48, 154-162.

[19] Cf. Carl Bridenbaugh: *Cities in the Wilderness* (New York: The Ronald Press, 1938).

[20] Cf. Frederick B. Tolles: *Meeting House and Counting House* (Chapel Hill, for Institute of Early American History and Culture at Williamsburg, Va., by University of N. Carolina Press, 1948).

Cotton Mather, and were actually rewritten by Franklin for Poor Richard. Philadelphia Quakers, like their Puritan brethren in Boston, sought wealth and position for "the Honour of God and Good of Mankind." They too considered that wealth conferred an obligation of "stewardship" upon the man with an estate. As William Penn expounded the doctrine, "But of all we call ours, we are most accountable to God and the publick for our estates: In this we are but stewards, and to hoard up all to ourselves is great injustice as well as ingratitude."

Most discussions of Franklin indicate that his career and social outlook are to be considered in sharp differentiation from the prevailing temper of Boston and New England generally, because Franklin's view of society was secular and not theological. It is certainly true that Franklin absorbed the "Protestant ethic" without maintaining any ties with the Calvinist theology in which it had been imbedded in the Boston of his youth. Franklin may, therefore, be considered to have demonstrated that "the Protestant ethic" itself could survive without that particular theology. Cotton Mather was not the only Boston preacher to have held ideas which were similar to Franklin's, but the fact remains that Franklin actually knew Mather, read his works, and more than once insisted on Mather's great influence upon him. Throughout all of Franklin's writings there appear phrases which maintain the spirit of the preachings of Mather and his contemporaries and which are testimony to their lasting effect upon him.

Franklin's program of good works and public improvements evoked a congenial and sympathetic response from the public-spirited citizens of Philadelphia. There was a regular plan of action. First there would be a paper read by Franklin at a meeting of the Junto, where it would be discussed; its contents would then be communicated to the associated Juntos; and, finally, one or more editorials would appear in Franklin's *Pennsylvania Gazette*. Once the public's attention had been called to the problem, some action might be expected, especially under the prodding of the newspaper and the network of Junto organizations. In this way, for example, Franklin succeeded in establishing a regular constabulary. He tells us how he "wrote a paper to be read in Junto" in which he proposed "the hiring of men to serve constantly in that business," their salaries to be paid by a property tax. "This idea, being approved by the Junto, was communicated to the other clubs, but as [if] arising in each of them; and though the plan was not immediately carried into execution ,yet, by preparing the minds of people for the change, it paved the way for the law obtained a few years after, when the members of our clubs were grown into more influence."[21] The Union Fire Company and the "academy" were introduced in this way and so were other "public improvements."

Franklin soon became a master of the art of promotion, and everyone with a project sought out his aid. When the Rev. Gilbert Tennent wished to obtain subscriptions for building a "meeting-house . . . for the use of a congregation he had gathered among the Presbyterians," he came to Franklin for assistance. But Franklin was "unwilling to make myself disagreeable to my fellow-citizens by too frequently soliciting their contributions," he explained to Tennent, though he was willing to give advice. "I advise you," he told Tennant, "to apply to all those whom you know will give something; next, to those whom you are un-

[21] Franklin's "Autobiography," Smyth, vol. 1, p. 352.

certain whether they will give anything or not, and show them
the list of those who have given; and, lastly, do not neglect
those who you are sure will give nothing, for in some of them you
may be mistaken." The advice was sound, Franklin was proud
to observe, and he pointed in evidence to "the capacious and
very elegant meeting-house that stands in Arch-street."[22]

In his "Autobiography," Franklin related the history of the
founding of the Pennsylvania Hospital as follows:[23]

> In 1751, Dr. Thomas Bond, a particular friend of mine,
> conceived the idea of establishing a hospital in Philadelphia
> (a very beneficent design, which has been ascribed to me,
> but was originally his), for the reception and cure of poor
> sick persons, whether inhabitants of the province or stran-
> gers. He was zealous and active in endeavouring to procure
> subscriptions for it, but the proposal being a novelty in
> America, and at first not well understood, he met with but
> small success.
>
> At length he came to me with the compliment that he
> found there was no such thing as carrying a public-spirited
> project through without my being concerned in it. "For,"
> says he, "I am often asked by those to whom I propose
> subscribing, Have you consulted Franklin upon this busi-
> ness? And what does he think of it? And when I tell them
> that I have not (supposing it rather out of your line), they
> do not subscribe, but say they will consider of it." I enquired
> into the nature and probable utility of his scheme, and re-

---

[22] *Ibid.*, p. 379.

[23] *Ibid.*, pp. 376-379. Franklin's own copy (in MS) of his autobiography has
been printed *verbatim et literatim* in Max Farrand (editor): *Benjamin
Franklin's Memoirs, parallel text edition, comprising the texts of Franklin's
original manuscript, the French translation by Louis Guillaume le Veillard,
the French translation published by Buisson, and the version edited by William
Temple Franklin, his grandson* (Berkeley: University of California Press, 1949).

ceiving from him a very satisfactory explanation, I not only subscribed to it myself, but engaged heartily in the design of procuring subscriptions from others. Previously, however, to the solicitation, I endeavoured to prepare the minds of the people by writing on the subject in the newspapers, which was my usual custom in such cases, but which he had omitted.

The subscriptions afterwards were more free and generous; but, beginning to flag, I saw they would be insufficient without some assistance from the Assembly, and therefore proposed to petition for it, which was done. The country members did not at first relish the project; they objected that it could only be serviceable to the city, and therefore the citizens alone should be at the expense of it; and they doubted whether the citizens themselves generally approved of it. My allegation on the contrary, that it met with such approbation as to leave no doubt of our being able to raise two thousand pounds by voluntary donations, they considered as a most extravagant supposition, and utterly impossible.

On this I formed my plan; and, asking leave to bring in a bill for incorporating the contributors according to the prayer of their petition, and granting them a blank sum of money, which leave was obtained chiefly on the consideration that the House could throw the bill out if they did not like it, I drew it so as to make the important clause a conditional one, viz., "And be it enacted, by the authority aforesaid, that when the said contributors shall have met and chosen their managers and treasurer, *and shall have raised by their contributions a capital stock of* value (the yearly interest of which is to be applied to the accommodating of the sick poor in the said hospital, free of charge for diet, attendance, advice, and medicines), *and shall make the same appear to the satisfaction of the speaker of the Assembly for the time being*, that *then* it shall and may be lawful for

[xx]

the said speaker, and he is hereby required, to sign an order on the provincial treasurer for the payment of two thousand pounds, in two yearly payments, to the treasurer of the said hospital, to be applied to the founding, building, and finishing of the same."

This condition carried the bill through; for the members, who had opposed the grant, and now conceived they might have the credit of being charitable without the expense, agreed to its passage; and then, in soliciting subscriptions among the people, we urged the conditional promise of the law as an additional motive to give, since every man's donation would be doubled; thus the clause worked both ways. The subscriptions accordingly soon exceeded the requisite sum, and we claimed and received the public gift, which enabled us to carry the design into execution. A convenient and handsome building was soon erected; the institution has by constant experience been found useful, and flourishes to this day; and I do not remember any of my political manoeuvres, the success of which gave me at the time more pleasure, or wherein, after thinking of it, I more easily excused myself for having made some use of cunning.

Franklin put into practice the very advice he gave to the Reverend Tennent; how well it succeeded!

In the book here reproduced, Franklin reprinted the newspaper articles about the needs for a hospital. They are not to be found in Franklin's works. The portion of the bill he "drew up" for the Assembly, quoted in the above extract from the "Autobiography," does not agree exactly with the text as printed by Franklin in his book. Franklin does not even mention the book in his "Autobiography." Carl Van Doren described the style of Franklin's *Some Account of the Pennsylvania Hospital* in these words: "His opening sentence is an example of homespun splendor hardly to be matched in the English language. The great sentences with which writers begin books commonly make use of flaming words; Franklin's words are all plain. His magic comes from his cadence and the emotion it implies."[24]

The history of the Pennsylvania Hospital has been rewritten many times in the two centuries since Franklin published his account. In 1951, on the occasion of the bicentenary of the founding, a number of historical articles were published.[25] Last

[24] In the concluding paper in *Meet Dr. Franklin* (Philadelphia: The Franklin Institute, 1943).

[25] Sydney P. Clark: *Pennsylvania Hospital—Since May 11, 1751: Two Hundred Years in Philadelphia* (New York: The Newcomen Society in North America, 1951), 44 pp.; Kenneth C. Crain: "Some Account of the Pennsylvania Hospital From its first Rise to the Beginning of the Year 1951," *Hospital Management*, vol. 71 (1951), pp. 3-23; Harriet C. Crane: "Treasures from the 18th Century Minutes," *The Pennsylvania Hospital Bulletin*, vol. 9 (Winter 1951-52), pp. 1-3, 6-8; E. B. Krumbhaar: Editorial: "The Pennsylvania Hospital," *Annals of Internal Medicine*, vol. 34 (1951), pp. 1280-1283; E. B. Krumbhaar: "Days at the Pennsylvania Hospital during its first century," *The American Journal of Medicine*, vol. 9 (1951), pp. 540-545; Francis R. Packard: "The practice of medicine in Philadelphia in the eighteenth century," *Annals of Medical History*, vol. 5 (1933), pp. 135-150; Mildred E. Whitcomb: "The country's first hospital puts service first," *The Modern Hospital* (May 1951), [reprint, 6 pp.]; Edmond G. Thomas (with John N. Hatfield, Florence M. Greim, and E. A. van Steenwyk): "Pennsylvania Hospital's 200 years," *Hospitals*, Journal of the American Hospital Association (May 1951), [reprint, 10 pp.]; "The Pennsylvania Hospital," 200th Annual Meeting Edition, *The Pennsylvania Hospital Bulletin*, vol. 9 (1951), pp. 1-23.

Three older publications contain further valuable material. One of these is Francis R. Packard: *Some Account of the Pennsylvania Hospital From its first Rise to the Beginning of the Year 1938* (ref. 3, above); another is Thomas G. Morton: *The History of the Pennsylvania Hospital* (ref. 28, below); and the third is George B. Wood: *An address on the occasion of the centennial celebration of the founding of the Pennsylvania Hospital* (Philadelphia: T. K. and P. G. Collins, printers, 1851).

year, Dr. Edward B. Krumbhaar contributed a brief history to a volume of essays on "historic Philadelphia."[26] In 1938, Dr. Francis R. Packard published a charming volume, written in Franklin's fashion and printed in a style of typography and format resembling Franklin's book, entitled *Some Account of the Pennsylvania Hospital from its first Rise to the Beginning of the Year 1938*,[27] thus supplementing and bringing up to date Dr. Thomas G. Morton's *History of the Pennsylvania Hospital, 1751-1895*.[28] This continuing stream of historical publications makes it unnecessary to recount here the story of the hospital from Franklin's day to ours. Still serving the needs of the community as it did two hundred years ago, the Pennsylvania Hospital stands as a monument to the collaboration of Franklin and Bond and the warm response they were able to evoke from their fellow citizens.

The original cornerstone, with text written by Franklin, can still be read plainly by visitors to the Pennsylvania Hospital. The text appears on the following page.

---

[26] Edward B. Krumbhaar: "The Pennsylvania Hospital," *Transactions of the American Philosophical Society*, vol. 43 (1953), pp. 237-246; this beautifully printed book, profusely illustrated and containing a map showing historic spots in Philadelphia, bears the general title: "Historic Philadelphia from the founding until the early 19th century: Papers dealing with its people and buildings, with an illustrative map."

[27] Cited in reference 3, above.

[28] Thomas G. Morton: *The History of the Pennsylvania Hospital, 1751-1895* (Philadelphia: Times Printing House, 1895).

SOME ACCOUNT OF THE PENNSYLVANIA HOSPITAL

IN THE YEAR OF CHRIST
MDCCLV.
GEORGE THE SECOND HAPPILY REIGNING
(FOR HE SOUGHT THE HAPPINESS OF HIS PEOPLE)
PHILADELPHIA FLOURISHING
(FOR ITS INHABITANTS WERE PUBLICK SPIRITED)
THIS BUILDING
BY THE BOUNTY OF THE GOVERNMENT,
AND OF MANY PRIVATE PERSONS
WAS PIOUSLY FOUNDED
FOR THE RELIEF OF THE SICK AND MISERABLE:
MAY THE GOD OF MERCIES
BLESS THE UNDERTAKING.

The second history of the Pennsylvania Hospital was a part of the campaign to raise funds in 1759 and the years immediately following. The needs were so much greater than the available funds that the situation was desperate; a petition to the Assembly in 1760 was unsuccessful. (Certainly the Managers missed the aid of Franklin, who was abroad in England on province business.) An appeal was sent to the *Pennsylvania Gazette* and prints or pictures were issued. Finally, a committee was appointed to write a book like Franklin's; the chairman was Samuel Rhoads. Called *Continuation of the Account of the Pennsylvania Hospital; from the first of May, 1754, to the fifth of May, 1761*,[29] the new book described the activities of the hospital, the care given to patients, and the sources of support and income along with the expenses. Whether the book was the effective

[29] See the description in Thomas G. Morton: *History* (ref. 28, above), pp. 46-49.

instrument in obtaining the needed funds, we do not know;[30] but the Assembly members visited the hospital, were favorably impressed by what they saw, and granted the sum of £3,000 to get the hospital out of its financial difficulties. Both Franklin's original publication and the *Continuation* were reprinted in 1817 at Philadelphia, "Printed at the Office of the United States' Gazette,"[31] and this edition seems to be even rarer than the original. Until now, neither part has ever been reprinted again.[32]

No one can turn the pages of Franklin's book without being struck by the modernity which characterizes every page, particularly the devices he employed to raise funds. Our admiration is aroused by the account of the noble physicians who served without compensation. The arguments advanced by Franklin in support of the hospital are compelling, and it is difficult to believe that they were conceived two hundred years ago and not yesterday. Here is presented, in the strongest terms, Franklin's thesis that an organized group of men working for a common goal can do more good in the world than if each man worked to

[30] Morton (ref. 28, above; p. 49) quotes the following document: "One of the books lately published containing a narrative of the management of the hospital for the last seven years including the account of the last year an abstract of the patients and a list of the contributors having been delivered to the Speaker and by him on Sept. 9th, 1761, communicated to the House of Representatives, William Allen, the Chief Justice and most of the members of the Assembly visited this hospital and after viewing the patients and inspecting the institution were pleased to express themselves much satisfied to observe the decency and economy of the house and that the good purposes of the charity were so carefully attended to."

[31] This reprint is described in Ford's *Franklin Bibliography* (ref. 2, above), p. 51, No. 100. I have never seen a copy.

[32] Some extracts have been printed in Cohen: *Benjamin Franklin* (ref. 13, above), pp. 177-188.

help his neighbors by himself. As an empiricist, Franklin was pleased to be able to demonstrate—by facts and figures—that the community as a whole would receive benefit from the new institution. His argument, that the function of a hospital is to restore sick individuals to their useful place in society, has a twentieth-century ring to it and seems especially appropriate to a free and democratic way of life. On the practical side, there is his suggestion that one of the major services rendered to the community by a hospital is to provide a training ground for young and inexperienced physicians. Physicians from the whole province of Pennsylvania would become acquainted with a greater variety of diseases than they might otherwise encounter from day to day, Franklin argued, and so the hospital would tend to raise the standards of medicine throughout the whole of Pennsylvania. As a staunch republican, Franklin was proud to observe that the hospital "gave to the beggar in America a degree of comfort and chance for recovery equal to that of a European prince in his palace." The hospital placed the patient in better and cleaner surroundings than a private home, and so was more conducive to the patient's recovery; even so, the cost of hospital care was only one-tenth of the cost of similar care in "private lodgings."

The title page of *Some Account of the Pennsylvania Hospital* indicates that the book was "printed by B. Franklin and D. Hall." It was characteristic of Franklin's shrewdness in business that he saw the great advantages that would derive from partnerships spread all over British America. In almost every instance,

Franklin was a "silent partner"; each shop operated under the name of the local printer. By 1743, Franklin had established three printing houses (in Philadelphia, Charleston, South Carolina, and New York) and was planning a fourth. Later establishments were set up in Antigua and Lancaster, New Jersey and Connecticut.[33] Hall, who became Franklin's partner in name as well as in fact, had learned the art of printing in Edinburgh and was working in London in 1743 when he was recommended to Franklin. Franklin invited him to come to Philadelphia and promised either to make him partner or give him a year's employment and a return passage to England should he wish to leave Philadelphia. David Hall proved to be "obliging, discreet, industrious, and honest." He became foreman of the printing shop in Philadelphia and in 1748 took over the major responsibility as partner. For eighteen years, until 1766, the firm was known as Franklin and Hall, and under Hall's management brought Franklin an average income of £467 per annum.[34]

Franklin did not in general create strikingly new typographical designs, although his best printing and that of his disciples has a style that has been described as "characteristic of Franklin," based on a feeling for the "integrity of type."[35] One of his first "excursions from the well-beaten path" was his *Cato Major*, published in 1744, and it may be conjectured that Hall had a hand in its design. On the other hand, most of the books issued under the Franklin and Hall imprint were inferior in workman-

[33] Cf. Lawrence C. Wroth: "Benjamin Franklin: The Printer at Work," *Meet Dr. Franklin* (Philadelphia: The Franklin Institute, 1943), p. 161; *The Colonial Printer* (Portland: The Southworth-Anthoensen Press, 1938).

[34] Cf. Carl Van Doren: *Benjamin Franklin* (ref. 4, above), p. 123.

[35] Cf. L. C. Wroth's article (ref. 33, above), p. 176.

ship to those earlier works printed by Franklin himself. We do not know how much of a hand Franklin actually had in the design of *Some Account of the Pennsylvania Hospital*, published in 1754, six years after his retirement. We know that in the fall of 1753 Franklin was again intensely interested in the art of printing, and suggested an improvement in printing presses. Perhaps, this revived concern for press problems in 1753 arose from a new contact with actual book-making, just before the 1754 publication about the Pennsylvania Hospital. It is doubtful whether David Hall could have designed this beautiful book by himself, and the typographical design must have been Franklin's. Considering the purpose for which the book was intended, and Franklin's strong personal interest in the project, it is hardly likely that Franklin would merely have turned over the copy to Hall without any further concern about the design and the presswork. In any event, this book displays some typical features of Franklin's printing, with a page well-designed but in too small a type for the size of the printed area and the length of line—a bitter disappointment after the "monumental title-page."[36] Even so, the pages have a certain typographical elegance. From one page to the next there is a variation in the form in which the printed material is presented. An engaging use is made of italics, capital and small capital letters, and running heads or captions. Even mere lists of names are presented in a contrasting manner (as on pages 32-33) and statistical data are printed (as on page 36) in an attractive fashion. Despite the limitations that derive from an economy in paper, and admitting that the type size might have been a little larger, there is no question but that Franklin's superb sense of craftsmanship made the book as a whole attractive to the eye and pleasant to read.

[36] *Ibid.*, p. 175.

SOME ACCOUNT OF THE PENNSYLVANIA HOSPITAL

The institution that this book was intended to serve was never "the lengthened shadow of one man." From the very beginning, the Pennsylvania Hospital thrived on the public-spirited devotion of a group of men with a common purpose, expressed in the original seal, bearing the device of the Good Samaritan conveying the sick man to an inn and the words "Take care of him, & I will repay thee." Many innovations in American medical teaching and public medicine originated in the Pennsylvania Hospital, among them clinical teaching, the out-patient department, and more recently "one of the first group practice clinics in America organized for comprehensive diagnostic service on a single-fee basis."[37] The Managers of the Pennsylvania Hospital have always considered the public interest first, making services available equally to all, rich or poor, and patients both afoot or abed. Even "home care" was provided, beginning in 1807, from the Hospital and in 1808 the policy was adopted that "the poor of Pennsylvania shall be vaccinated gratis, if they will call at the Hospital."[38] Now in its third century, the Pennsylvania Hospital can boast that more than 2,500,000 persons have been treated, and that only one out of every three has paid the full cost of treatment. Today the Hospital encompasses many departments and institutions; the original site now being known as the Department for Sick and Injured and the original building being reduced to but one of the units in that great block of buildings on Eighth Street between Spruce and Pine, still in active service.

Conceived by Dr. Thomas Bond, brought into existence

[37] Dean A. Clark: "Two Centuries of Service—What of the Next?" *The Pennsylvania Hospital Bulletin*, vol. 9, no. 3 (1951), pp. 2-3.
[38] *Ibid.*, p. 4.

SOME ACCOUNT OF THE PENNSYLVANIA HOSPITAL

through the aid of Benjamin Franklin, the Pennsylvania Hospital continues to serve the country as the pioneer example that the efforts of free man can produce permanent institutions of public benefit. As we turn the pages of the first appeal for public support of the Pennsylvania Hospital, we may recapture the original spirit that motivated the men of Franklin's day to minister to the needs of their neighbors. Poor Richard said in 1738, "If you would not be forgotten as soon as you are dead and rotten, either write things worth reading or do things worth the writing." The Pennsylvania Hospital and Franklin's book about it indicate that he did both. The early record of the Pennsylvania Hospital speaks for itself in Franklin's pages, which remind us of our own obligation to support institutions dedicated to the needs of the less fortunate members of the community. The inaugural history of America's first permanent hospital, written by America's foremost citizen, seems to be a tract for our own times. As we read it, we appreciate anew how many aspects of our American life were influenced by the precepts and example of Benjamin Franklin: the pioneer of the American personality.

Some Account of the Pennsylvania Hospital

SOME

ACCOUNT

OF THE

Pennsylvania Hospital;

From its first RISE, to the Beginning
of the *Fifth Month*, called *May*, 1754.

PHILADELPHIA:
Printed by B. FRANKLIN, and D. HALL. MDCCLIV.

SOME

ACCOUNT

OF THE

PENNSYLVANIA *HOSPITAL.*

ABOUT the End of the Year 1750, some Persons, who had frequent Opportunities of obferving the Diſtreſs of ſuch diſtemper'd Poor as from Time to Time came to *Philadelphia*, for the Advice and Aſſiſtance of the Phyſicians and Surgeons of that City; how difficult it was for them to procure ſuitable Lodgings, and other Conveniences proper for their reſpective Caſes, and how expenſive the Providing good and careful Nurſes, and other Attendants, for want whereof, many muſt ſuffer greatly, and ſome probably periſh, that might otherwiſe have been reſtored to Health and Comfort, and become uſeful to them-ſelves, their Families, and the Publick, for many Years after; and conſidering more-over, that even the poor Inhabitants of this City, tho' they had Homes, yet were therein but badly accommodated in Sickneſs, and could not be ſo well and ſo eaſily taken Care of in their ſeparate Habitations, as they might be in one convenient Houſe, under one Inſpection, and in the Hands of ſkilful Practitioners; and ſeveral of the Inhabitants of the Province, who unhappily became diſorder'd in their Senſes, wander'd about, to the Terror of their Neighbours, there being no Place (except the Houſe of Correction) in which they might be confined, and ſubjected to proper Management for their Recovery, and that Houſe was by no Means fitted for ſuch Purpoſes; did charitably conſult together, and confer with their Friends and Ac-quaintances, on the beſt Means of relieving the Diſtreſſed, under thoſe Circum-ſtances; and an Infirmary, or Hoſpital, in the Manner of ſeveral lately eſtabliſhed in *Great-Britain*, being propoſed, was ſo generally approved, that there was Reaſon to expect a conſiderable Subſcription from the Inhabitants of this City, towards the Support of ſuch an Hoſpital; but the Expence of erecting a Building ſufficiently large and commodious for the Purpoſe, it was thought would be too heavy, unleſs the Subſcription could be made general through the Province, and ſome Aſſiſtance

could

could be obtained from the Assembly; the following Petition was therefore drawn, and presented to the House on the 23d of *January*, 1750-51.

To the Honourable House of REPRESENTATIVES *of the Province of* Pennsylvania,

The PETITION *of sundry Inhabitants of the said Province.*

Humbly sheweth,

' THAT with the Numbers of People the Number of Lunaticks, or Per-
' sons distemper'd in Mind, and deprived of their rational Faculties, hath
' greatly encreased in this Province.

' THAT some of them going at large, are a Terror to their Neighbours, who are
' daily apprehensive of the Violences they may commit ; and others are continually
' wasting their Substance, to the great Injury of themselves and Families, ill disposed
' Persons wickedly taking Advantage of their unhappy Condition, and drawing them
' into unreasonable Bargains, &c.

' THAT few or none of them are so sensible of their Condition as to submit volun-
' tarily to the Treatment their respective Cases require, and therefore continue in the
' same deplorable State during their Lives ; whereas it has been found, by the Ex-
' perience of many Years, that above two Thirds of the mad People received into
' *Bethlehem* Hospital, and there treated properly, have been perfectly cured.

' YOUR Petitioners beg Leave farther to represent, that tho' the good Laws of
' this Province have made many compassionate and charitable Provisions for the Re-
' lief of the Poor, yet something farther seems wanting in Favour of such whose
' Poverty is made more miserable by the additional Weight of a grievous Disease,
' from which they might easily be relieved, if they were not situated at too great a
' Distance from regular Advice and Assistance, whereby many languish out their
' Lives, tortur'd perhaps with the Stone, devour'd by the Cancer, depriv'd of Sight
' by Cataracts, or gradually decaying by loathsome Distempers ; who, if the Ex-
' pence in the present Manner of nursing and attending them separately when they
' come to Town, were not so discouraging, might again, by the judicious Assistance
' of Physick and Surgery, be enabled to taste the Blessings of Health, and be made
' in a few Weeks useful Members of the Community, able to provide for themselves
' and Families.

' THE kind Care our Assemblies have heretofore taken for the Relief of sick and
' distemper'd Strangers, by providing a Place for their Reception and Accommoda-
' tion, leaves us no Room to doubt their shewing an equal tender Concern for the
' Inhabitants. And we hope they will be of Opinion with us, that a small Provincial
' Hospital, erected and put under proper Regulations, in the Care of Persons to be
' appointed by this House, or otherwise, as they shall think meet, with Power to re-
' ceive and apply the charitable Benefactions of good People towards enlarging and
' supporting the same, and some other Provisions in a Law for the Purposes above-
' mentioned, will be a good Work, acceptable to G O D, and to all the good People
' they represent.

' WE therefore humbly recommend the Premises to their serious Consideration.'

ON

ON the second Reading of the Petition, *January* 29, the House gave Leave to the Petitioners to bring in a Bill, which was read the first Time on the first of *February*. For some Time it was doubtful whether the Bill would not miscarry, many of the Members not readily conceiving the Necessity or Usefulness of the Design ; and apprehending moreover, that the Expence of paying Physicians and Surgeons, would eat up the whole of any Fund that could be reasonably expected to be raised ; but three of the Profession, *viz.* Doctors *Lloyd Zachary, Thomas Bond,* and *Phineas Bond,* generously offering to attend the Hospital *gratis* for three Years, and the other Objections being by Degrees got over, the Bill, on the seventh of the same Month, passed the House, *Nemine Contradicente,* and in *May* following it received the Governor's Assent, and was enacted into a Law, as follows.

An ACT *to encourage the Establishing of an* HOSPITAL *for the Relief of the Sick Poor of this Province, and for the Reception and Cure of Lunaticks.*

' WHEREAS the saving and restoring useful and laborious Members to a
' Community, is a Work of publick Service, and the Relief of the Sick
' Poor is not only an Act of Humanity, but a religious Duty ; and whereas there
' are frequently, in many Parts of this Province, poor distemper'd Persons, who lan-
' guish long in Pain and Misery under various Disorders of Body and Mind, and
' being scattered abroad in different and very distant Habitations, cannot have the
' Benefit of regular Advice, Attendance, Lodging, Diet and Medicines, but at a
' great Expence, and therefore often suffer for want thereof; which Inconveniency
' might be happily removed, by collecting the Patients into one common Provincial
' Hospital, properly disposed and appointed, where they may be comfortably sub-
' sisted, and their Health taken Care of at a small Charge, and by the Blessing of
' GOD on the Endeavours of skilful Physicians and Surgeons, their Diseases may
' be cured and removed. And whereas it is represented to this Assembly, that there
' is a charitable Disposition in divers Inhabitants of this Province to contribute largely
' towards so good a Work, if such Contributors might be incorporated with proper
' Powers and Privileges for carrying on and compleating the same, and some Part of
' the Publick Money given and appropriated to the Providing a suitable Building for
' the Purposes aforesaid.
' THEREFORE, for the Encouragement of so useful, pious and charitable a De-
' sign, we pray that it may be enacted, And be it enacted by the Honourable JAMES
' HAMILTON, Esquire, Lieutenant-Governor under the Honourable *THOMAS*
' *PENN,* and *RICHARD PENN,* Esquires, true and absolute Proprietaries
' of the Province of *Pennsylvania,* and Counties of *New-Castle, Kent* and *Sussex,* up-
' on *Delaware,* by and with the Advice and Consent of the Representatives of the
' Freemen of the said Province in General Assembly met, and by the Authority of the
' same, That it shall and may be lawful to and for all Persons, each of whom shall
' have contributed or subscribed the Sum of *Ten Pounds* or more, towards founding an
' Hospital, for the Reception and Relief of Lunaticks, and other distemper'd and
' sick Poor within this Province, or as many of them as shall think fit to assemble and
' meet on the first Day of the Month called *July* next ; and for all Persons who shall
' thereafter

' thereafter contribute the like Sum of *Ten Pounds* or more (together with the faid firft
' Subfcribers) or fo many of them as fhall think fit to affemble and meet on the fecond
' Day of the firft Week, in the Month called *May*, yearly for ever, at fome conve-
' nient Place in the City of *Philadelphia*, then and there to elect by Ballot, twelve fit
' and fuitable Perfons of their own Number to be Managers of the faid Contribution
' and Hofpital, and one other Perfon to be Treafurer of the fame, until the next
' Election ; and farther, to make fuch Laws, Rules and Orders, as fhall appear to
' them the faid Contributors met, or the major Part of them, to be good, ufeful
' and neceffary, for the well governing, ordering and regulating the faid Hofpital,
' and for the Regulation of the future Elections of Managers, Treafurer, and other
' neceffary Officers and Minifters thereof, and for limiting and appointing their Num-
' ber, Truft, and Authority, and generally for the well ordering all other Things con-
' cerning the Government, Eftate, Goods, Lands, Revenues, as alfo all the Bufinefs
' and Affairs of the faid Hofpital : All which Laws, Rules and Orders, fo to be
' made as aforefaid, fhall be from Time to Time inviolably obferved by all concern'd,
' according to the Tenor and Effect of them, provided they be not repugnant to
' the Laws of *England* or this Government, and are approved by the Chief
' Juftice, the Speaker of the Affembly, and the Attorney-General of this Province
' for the Time being, under their Hands and Seals. And the faid Contributors fhall
' be, and are hereby made a Body Corporate in Law, to all Intents and Pur-
' pofes, and fhall have perpetual Succeffion, and may fue, or be fued, plead, or be
' impleaded, by the Name of *The Contributors to the* Pennfylvania *Hofpital*, in all
' Courts of Judicature within this Province, and by that Name, fhall and may re-
' ceive and take any Lands, Tenements, or Hereditaments, not exceeding the year-
' ly Value of *One Thoufand Pounds*, of the Gift, Alienation, Bequeft, or Devife of
' any Perfon or Perfons whomfoever ; and of any Goods or Chattels whatfoever ; and
' the faid Contributors are hereby impower'd to have and ufe one common Seal in
' their Affairs, and the fame at their Pleafure to change and alter.

' PROVIDED neverthelefs, That no General Meeting of the faid Contributors, nor
' any Perfons acting under them, fhall employ any Money or other Eftate, exprefly
' given or added to the Capital Stock of the faid Hofpital, in any other Way than
' by applying its annual Intereft or Rent towards the Entertainment and Care of the
' fick and diftemper'd Poor, that fhall be from Time to Time brought and placed
' therein, for the Cure of their Difeafes, from any Part of this Province, without
' Partiality or Preference.

' AND for the further Encouragement of this beneficent Undertaking, Be it enact-
' ed by the Authority aforefaid, That when the faid Contributors fhall have met and
' chofen their Managers and Treafurer as aforefaid, and fhall have raifed by their Con-
' tributions, a Capital Stock of *Two Thoufand Pounds* Value (the yearly Intereft or
' Rent of which is to be applied to the Accommodating of the Sick Poor in the faid
' Hofpital, free of Charge for Diet, Attendance, Advice and Medicines) and fhall
' make the fame appear to the Satisfaction of the Speaker of the Affembly for the
' Time being ; that then it fhall and may be lawful for the faid Speaker of the Af-
' fembly, and he is hereby required to fign an Order or Orders on the Provincial
' Treafurer, or Truftees of the Loan-Office, for the Payment of *Two Thoufand*
' *Pounds*,

' *Pounds*, in two yearly Payments, to the Treasurer of the said Hospital, to be ap-
' plied to the Founding, Building, and Furnishing of the same.
' AND be it further enacted by the Authority aforesaid, That the Accounts of the
' Disbursements of the said *Two Thousand Pounds*, so ordered by the Speaker of the
' Assembly aforesaid, or any Part thereof that shall be hereafter expended, as the
' Case may be, and of the Rents, Products, and Interests of any real or personal
' Estates or Sums of Money charitably given to the Use of the said Hospital, toge-
' ther with a List of such Donations, shall be fairly drawn out and published annu-
' ally in the *Gazette*, or other News-papers : And the Managers of the said Hospital
' shall at all Times, when required, submit the Books, Accounts, Affairs, and Œco-
' nomy thereof, to the Inspection and free Examination of such Visitors as may from
' Time to Time be appointed by the Assembly of this Province, to visit and inspect
' the same.
' PROVIDED always, and it is hereby further enacted by the Authority afore-
' said, That if at any Time hereafter, there should not be a constant Succession of
' Contributors to meet yearly and chuse Managers as aforesaid, then the said Hospi-
' tal, and the Estate and Affairs thereof, shall be in the Management, and under
' the Direction of such Persons as shall be from Time to Time appointed by Act of
' General Assembly of this Province for that Purpose.'

As soon as the Law was published, the Promoters of the Design set on Foot a
Subscription, which in a short Time amounted to considerable more than the Sum
required by the Act. And on the First of the Month called *July*, 1751, a Majority of the Contributors met at the State-House in *Philadelphia*, and pursuant to
the Act chose by Ballot twelve Managers, and a Treasurer, *viz.*

MANAGERS,

JOSHUA CROSBY,	SAMUEL RHODES,
BENJAMIN FRANKLIN,	HUGH ROBERTS,
THOMAS BOND,	JOSEPH MORRIS,
SAMUEL HAZARD,	JOHN SMITH,
RICHARD PETERS,	EVAN MORGAN,
ISRAEL PEMBERTON, junior,	CHARLES NORRIS.

TREASURER, JOHN REYNELL.

THE Managers met soon after the Choice, and viewed several Spots of Ground
in and near the City, which were thought suitable to erect Buildings on for this Purpose ; and agreeing in Judgment, that one particular Lot, belonging to the Proprietaries, would suit as well or better than any other, they drew up the following re-
spectful Address, and sent it (with the following Letter) to *Thomas Hyam*, and *Sylvanus Bevan*, to be presented by them to the Proprietaries. And that it may be seen
at one View, what has been hitherto done in that Affair, it is thought proper to add
the Answers the Managers received from their Agents, and other Papers relative
thereto.

To

To the Honourable *THOMAS PENN*, and *RICHARD PENN*, Efquires, Proprietaries of the Province of *Pennfylvania*, &c.

The A D D R E S S of the Managers of the *Pennfylvania* Hofpital.

May it pleafe the Proprietaries,

IT *hath been long obferved, that this your Province, remarkable for the Goodnefs of its Conftitution, Laws and Government, and many other Advantages, is yet deficient of a common Hofpital or Infirmary, for the Relief of fuch Poor as are afflicted with curable Difeafes.*

YOUR good People here, to fupply this Defect, and out of a tender charitable Regard for their Fellow-creatures, have voluntarily fubfcribed, and are ftill fubfcribing, large Sums towards a Stock for the Support of fuch an Hofpital: And the General Affembly being petitioned by a Number of the Inhabitants of all Ranks and Denominations, have paffed an Act to encourage the fame, and granted Two Thoufand Pounds *for the Founding, Building, and Furnifhing thereof.*

IN Purfuance of that Act, we the Subfcribers were, on the firft of this Inftant, chofen by the Contributors to be Managers of the faid Hofpital, and think it our Duty to take this firft Opportunity of laying the Affair before our Proprietaries, in humble Confidence that fo good and pious an Undertaking will not fail of their Approbation; hoping withal, from the accuftomed Bounty of the Proprietary Family, in encouraging former Defigns of publick Utility to the People of their Province, the prefent will alfo receive their kind Affiftance; and as private Perfons raife a Stock to fupport the Hofpital, and the Affembly build the Houfe, fo (that all concerned in the Province may fhare in the Honour, Merit and Pleafure of promoting fo good a Work) the Proprietaries will be pleafed to favour us with the Grant of a Piece of Ground for the Buildings, and their neceffary Accommodations.

IF any Thing fhould occur to the Proprietaries, that they may think of Service with refpect to the Management or Rules of the Hofpital, we fhould be obliged to them for their Sentiments, being defirous that what falls within our Duty, may be done to the greateft Advantage for the Publick.

We are, with great Refpect,

Philadelphia, July 6, 1751.   Your very affectionate Friends,

JOSHUA CROSBY,   SAMUEL RHODES,
BENJAMIN FRANKLIN,   JOSEPH MORRIS,
THOMAS BOND,   JOHN SMITH,
SAMUEL HAZARD,   EVAN MORGAN.
ISRAEL PEMBERTON, junior, CHARLES NORRIS.
HUGH ROBERTS.

Efteemed

Esteemed Friends, Thomas Hyam,   *Philadelphia,* *July* 6, 1751.
    and Silvanus Bevan,

'THE Opinion we have of your beneficent Principles, induces us to make
'this Application to you, and we hope the Opportunity of exerting your Ten-
'derness to the Afflicted and Distressed, will be so acceptable, as to render any Apo-
'logy unnecessary for our Freedom in requesting your Friendship in delivering and sol-
'liciting the Address we herewith send to our Proprietaries, THOMAS and RICHARD
'PENN.

' THE Circumstances of this Province have, in a few Years past, been much al-
'ter'd, by the Addition of a great Number of Persons who arrive here from several
'Parts of *Europe,* many of whom are poor, and settle in remote Parts of the Coun-
'try, where suitable Provision cannot be made for their Relief from the various Dis-
'orders of Body and Mind some of them labour under ; the Consideration of which
'hath lately rais'd in many of the Inhabitants of this City a benevolent Concern, and
'engaged them to apply for the Assistance of the Legislature, by whom a Law is pas-
'sed, and some Provision made out of the Provincial Treasury for the Erecting a
'publick Hospital or Infirmary, under the Direction of a Corporation, by whom we
'have lately been elected the Managers ; but as the publick Funds are not sufficient to
'answer the Expence of endowing it, a charitable Subscription for that Purpose hath
'been propos'd and begun with good Success. The Necessity and Advantages of this
'Institution are so apparent, that Persons of all Ranks unite very heartily in promoting
'it ; and as several of our most eminent Physicians and Surgeons have freely offered
'their Service for some Years, we have good Grounds to expect that this Under-
'taking may be of general Service much sooner than was at first expected, and that
'our Legislature will soon make a further Provision for the Building, which we ap-
'prehend it will be prudent to contrive and erect in such Manner, as to admit of such
'Additions as the future State of the Province may require. The principal Dif-
'ficulty we now labour under, is the Want of a commodious Lot of Ground in
'a healthy Situation ; for (tho' we have so great Encouragement as we have men-
'tion'd) we cannot flatter ourselves with speedily raising a Sum sufficient to enable
'us to provide for all other necessary Charges, and to purchase a suitable Piece of
'Ground so near the built Part of the City, as the constant Attendance of the Phy-
'sicians, and other Considerations, will necessarily require : We are therefore under the
'Necessity of laying the State of our Case before our Proprietaries, and we hope the
'same Motives which have induced others, will have due Weight with them to pro-
'mote this good Work, and that they will generously direct a Piece of Ground to be
'allotted for this Service.

' THERE are several Lots in different Parts of this City very suitable, but from
'their Situation, *&c.* are of great Value for other Purposes; we have therefore
'thought of one, which is in a Part of the Town quite unimproved, and where, in
'all Probability, there will be the Conveniency of an open Air for many Years; it is
'the vacant Part of the Square between the *Ninth* and *Tenth-streets* from *Delaware,*
'on the *South* Side of *Mulberry-street,* and is 396 Feet *East* and *West,* and 360 Feet
'*North* and *South.* The Lots in this Part of the City have not advanced in Value

B   ' for

' for several Years past, and are not likely to be soon settled; so that we are in Hopes,
' if you will favour us with your Application for this Piece of Ground, you will meet
' with no Difficulty in obtaining it.

' THE Interest of the Proprietaries and People are so nearly connected, that it
' seems to us self-evident that they mutually share in whatever contributes to the Pro-
' sperity and Advantage of the Province; which Consideration, added to the Satisfac-
' tion arising from Acts of Charity and Benevolence, will, we hope, have so much
' Weight with them, as to render any other Argument superfluous; but as your own
' Prudence will suggest to you the most effectual Method of solliciting this Address
' succesfully, we rely thereon so much, as to think it unnecessary to add any Thing
' more on this Occasion, than that your Friendship therein will be exceedingly grateful
' to us, and our Fellow-citizens in general; and next to obtaining the Lot we ask
' for, the most agreeable Service you can do us, is to obtain a speedy Answer;
' for the Promoting this Undertaking appears to us so necessary, that all concerned
' therein are unanimous in determining to prepare for the Building early in the Spring
' next Year.'

We are, with much Respect,

Signed as before.   *Your obliged and real Friends.*

Esteemed Friends,   London, 18th 1st Mo. 1752.

WE received yours the Sixth *July* past, and the Address which it brought was
by us delivered to THOMAS PENN, *Esquire, unto which we most readily joined
what Interest we have with him and his Brother, to grant your Request of a
Piece of Ground, whereon to build the proposed Hospital in your City; and we make no
Doubt but* Joshua Crosby *hath informed you of what his Answer was, and also of what*
Thomas Hyam *and Son wrote him from Time to Time on the Subject; and now we have
the Pleasure to acquaint you, that Yesterday we received a Letter from him granting your
Request, a Copy whereof is here under.*

We are your assured Friends,

To the Managers of the *Penn-*   THOMAS HYAM,
sylvania Hospital.   SYLVANUS BEVAN.

Gentlemen,   London, January 17, 1752.

YOU *may inform the Directors of the Hospital at* Philadelphia, *that we sent Orders
to the Governor, the Nineteenth of* December, *by Way of* New-England, *to
grant them a Piece of Ground to build the Hospital upon, tho' not the Piece they ask'd, yet
one of the same Size, and when, if it should be necessary, we can grant them an Addition.*

I am, Gentlemen,

Your affectionate Friend,

To Messieurs *Sylvanus Bevan,*
and *Thomas Hyam,*   THOMAS PENN.

THE

THE Governor was pleafed to favour the Managers with a Copy of the Inftruc-
tions he received upon this Occafion, which, after due Confideration, they made fome
Obfervations upon, and fent to their Agents. A Copy of thefe feveral Papers here
follow in their Order.

THOMAS PENN, and *RICHARD PENN*, *true and abfolute
Proprietaries of the Province of* Pennfylvania, *and of the Counties of* New-Caftle,
Kent, *and* Suffex, *on* Delaware, *in* America :

To JAMES HAMILTON, *Efq; our Lieutenant-Governor of our faid Province, and Counties, and to all other Perfons whom thefe Prefents may concern, greeting.*

'   WHEREAS it hath been reprefented unto us, that there is a Want
'   in our faid Province of a common Hofpital or Infirmary, for the Relief of
' fuch Poor as are afflicted with curable Difeafes ; and that many of the good In-
' habitants thereof, to fupply that Defect, and out of a tender and charitable Regard
' to their Fellow-creatures, had voluntarily fubfcribed, and were ftill fubfcribing, large
' Sums of Money, towards a Stock for the Support of fuch an Hofpital ; and that
' the Affembly there, being petitioned by a Number of the Inhabitants of all Ranks
' and Denominations, had already granted *Two Thoufand Pounds*, for the Founding,
' Building and Furnifhing thereof ; and that the Perfons who had contributed towards
' the Stock thereof, or many of them, had, in the Month of *July* laft paft, chofen
' certain Perfons to be Managers of the faid intended Hofpital.
'   AND whereas the faid Managers have addreffed us, laying the faid Affair before
' us, in Confidence that fo good and pious an Undertaking would not fail of our
' Approbation, and hoping, from the accuftom'd Bounty of our Family in encourag-
' ing former Defigns of publick Utility to the People of our faid Province, the pre-
' fent would alfo receive our kind Affiftance ; and that as private Perfons raifed the
' Stock to fupport the Hofpital, and the Affembly were to build the Houfe, fo that
' we would be pleafed to favour the faid Managers with the Grant of a Piece of
' Ground for the Buildings and neceffary Accommodations for the faid Hofpital ; and
' alfo requefting our Sentiments, if any Thing fhould occur to us that we might think
' of Service with refpect to the Management or Rules of the faid Hofpital :
'   KNOW ye therefore, that we, having taken the Premifes into our Confideration,
' and approving and greatly favouring the faid general Scheme and Intention, and
' being defirous to aid and affift the fame, as conceiving that the due Execution there-
' of may tend to the Relief of many poor and neceffitous Perfons in our faid Pro-
' vince, and to the general Benefit and Advantage of the fame, have refolved to in-
' corporate the prefent and future Subfcribers by our Grant of Incorporation ; and at
' the fame time to grant unto fuch Corporation fo incorporated, a valuable Tract of
' Land in a proper Place within our good City of *Philadelphia*.
'   IN order whereto, we do by thefe Prefents give, grant, and commit unto you,
' our faid Lieutenant-Governor, full Power, Commiffion, and Authority, by one
' Inftrument or Grant of Incorporation, to be iffued in our Names, and to be fealed
' with the Great Seal of our faid Province, to incorporate and erect into a Body Po-

' litick

‘ litick or Corporate, by fuch Name or Title as to you fhall feem moft apt and
‘ convenient, all and every fuch Perfons, who already have fubfcribed and paid, or
‘ at any Time hereafter fhall fubfcribe and pay the Sum of *Ten Pounds* or more,
‘ of current Money of our faid Province, towards the Founding and Eftablifhing an
‘ Hofpital for the Reception and Relief of Lunaticks, and other diftemper’d and
‘ fick Poor within our faid Province, fuch Corporation to have Continuance to fuch
‘ Contributors and their Succeffors for ever ; and to grant all ufual, common, pro-
‘ per and reafonable Powers of a Corporation unto fuch Corporation, and their Suc-
‘ ceffors ; and particularly for the Making of fuch reafonable and lawful By-Laws,
‘ Rules and Orders, as to the faid Corporation, or the major Part of them, when duly
‘ affembled in fuch Manner as fhall be therein appointed, fhall feem ufeful and neceffary
‘ for the well-ordering, regulating and governing the faid Hofpital ; for the Regula-
‘ tion of the future Elections of Managers, Treafurer or Treafurers, and other necef-
‘ fary Officers and Minifters thereof ; for limiting their Numbers, Trufts and Authori-
‘ ties, and the Times and Durations of their refpective Continuance in their Offices,
‘ and the Caufes and Manner of removing any of them (if Occafion fhould require)
‘ and generally, for the well-ordering all other Matters and Things, any way re-
‘ lating to or concerning the good Government, Eftate, Lands, Rents, Revenues,
‘ Intereft, Monies and Goods, and all other the Bufinefs and Affairs of the faid
‘ Hofpital, and of the Poor therein, and of the Officers and Minifters thereof.
‘ And alfo to grant, that all fuch By-Laws, Rules and Orders, fo to be made as
‘ aforefaid, fhall be from Time to Time inviolably obferv’d by all concerned, ac-
‘ cording to the Tenor and Effect of them, provided they be reafonable in them-
‘ felves, not repugnant to the Laws of *Great-Britain*, or of our faid Province,
‘ and be firft approved by us, or fuch of us, our Heirs or Affigns, Proprietaries of
‘ our faid Province, as fhall for the Time being be in *America*, and by the Chief Juftice,
‘ and Speaker of the Affembly for the Time being, under our and their Hands and
‘ Seals, in cafe we, or either of us, or the Heirs or Affigns of us, or of either of us,
‘ or any of them, fhall for the Time being happen to be in *America* ; but in cafe we,
‘ or either of us, nor any of the Heirs or Affigns of either of us, Proprietaries of our
‘ faid Province, fhall happen from Time to Time to be in *America*, then being firft
‘ approved by and under the Hands and Seals of the Governor or Lieutenant-Go-
‘ vernor, the Chief Juftice, the Speaker of the Affembly, and the Attorney-Gene-
‘ ral of our faid Province for the Time being, or by any three of them. And alfo
‘ to grant and appoint fuch Perfons to be prefent and immediate Officers of fuch
‘ Corporation (until a future Election of new Ones) as have already been chofen or
‘ appointed by the Subfcribers thereto ; and to grant Power to the faid Corporation,
‘ and to their Succeffors, to take and receive, and to hold and enjoy, for the Ufe
‘ of the faid Corporation, any Lands, Tenements or Hereditaments within our faid
‘ Province, not exceeding in the whole the yearly Value of *One Thoufand Pounds* at
‘ the Time of fuch taking of the Gift, Grant, Alienation, Bequeft or Devife of any
‘ Perfon or Perfons whatfoever ; and alfo to take, receive, hold and enjoy, any
‘ Goods or Chattels, to any Value whatfoever : And to grant unto the faid Corpo-
‘ ration Power to ufe a common Seal for the Bufinefs of the faid Corporation, and
‘ the fame at Pleafure to alter and change ; but you are in fuch our Grant of Incor-
‘ poration

' poration to infert one or more exprefs Provifoes and Conditions, that no General
' Meeting of the Members of fuch Corporation, or any Perfons acting under them,
' fhall fell or convert into Money, any real Eftate, given or to be given to the faid
' Corporation (unlefs directed fo to do by the Donor or Donors of the fame) nor
' fhall employ or difpofe of any Principal Money or other Effects, which are or
' fhall be given or added for the Purpofe of encreafing of the Capital Stock of the
' faid Corporation, in any other Manner than by applying the annual Rent, Reve-
' nue, Income, or Intereft of the fame, towards the Entertainment and Cure of the
' fick and diftemper'd Poor, that fhall from Time to Time be brought and placed
' in or under the Care of the faid Hofpital, and the Officers and Minifters thereof,
' for the Cure of their Difeafes, from any Part of our faid Province, without Par-
' tiality or Preference. And alfo that fair, full and plain Accounts in Writing, of all
' Subfcriptions, Benefactions, Donations, and Gifts of every Kind to the faid Cor-
' poration, and of the Difpofal, Employment and Difburfements of the fame, and
' of the Rents, Revenues, Incomes, Intereft and Produce arifing therefrom, and
' of the Difpofal thereof, and of all Salaries paid to any Officers or Servants, fhall
' conftantly lay open in fome publick Part of the Hofpital, for the free View and
' Infpection, at all Times in the Day, of any Subfcriber or Contributor ; and that
' an Account of the fame, figned by three or more of the Managers, be, from
' Time to Time, once in the Month of *October*, in every Year, publifhed in the
' *Gazette*, or other News-paper, printed in our faid Province, for the Information of
' all Perfons. And that the Books, Accounts, Affairs, Œconomy, Difpofition,
' and Management of the faid Hofpital, and of all the Eftate, Rents, Revenues,
' and Intereft thereof, and of all the Managers, Treafurers, Officers, Minifters
' and Servants thereof, and every Matter and Thing relating to the fame, or to any
' of them, and all Abufes concerning the fame (if any fuch fhould ever happen)
' fhall at all Times be fubject to the Infpection, free Examination and Reformation
' of fuch Vifitors, not exceeding four in Number, as we, our Heirs or Affigns,
' Proprietaries of the faid Province, or the Lieutenant-Governor of the faid Province
' for the Time being, fhall from Time to Time appoint, fo as the Chief Juftice,
' and the Speaker of the Affembly of our faid Province for the Time being, be al-
' ways two of fuch Vifitors.

' A N D we do hereby give, grant and commit to you, our faid Lieutenant-Gover-
' nor, further Power, Commiffion and Authority, in and by the fame Inftrument or
' Grant of Incorporation to be fo iffued as aforefaid, to give and grant unto, and for
' the Ufe of the faid Corporation, and their Succeffors for ever, all that Part of the
' Square or Parcel of vacant Land, in our faid City of *Philadelphia*, herein after de-
' fcribed; *That is to fay*, All that Piece or Parcel of Land fituated, lying and being
' on the *North* Side of *Saffafras-ftreet*, between *Sixth* and *Seventh-ftreets* from *Dela-*
' *ware*, containing from *Eaft* to *Weft* on *Saffafras-ftreet* Three Hundred and Ninety-
' fix Feet, or thereabouts, little more or lefs, and from *South* to *North*, on *Sixth* and
' *Seventh-ftreets*, Three Hundred Feet, and bounding Northwards on other vacant
' Land, Part of the fame Square, referved to us, to hold unto, and to the Ufe of the
' faid Corporation and their Succeffors, to and for the Ufe of the faid Hofpital for
' ever, rendering to the Hands of our Receiver-General, and of the Receiver-General

'ral of us, our Heirs, or Affigns, Proprietaries of the faid Province for the Time be-
'ing, in our faid Province, for our Ufe, the yearly Rent of *Five Shillings* of lawful
'Money of *Great-Britain*, on the firft Day of *March* in each and every Year henceforth
'for ever, under a declared and exprefs Provifoe and Condition to be contained in fuch
'Grant of Incorporation, that if, at any Time hereafter, there fhall not be a conftant
'Succeffion of Contributors to meet yearly and choofe Managers and Officers, then
'the faid Tract of Land thereby to be granted, fhall revert and return to us, our Heirs
'and Affigns, Proprietaries of our faid Province, as in our firft and former Eftate.
'And you are to infert in fuch Grant, all fuch other proper Claufes and Matters not
'contrary to, or inconfiftent with, the Directions hereby given, as to you fhall feem
'proper and reafonable; and particularly for the Enrolment of the faid Grant in the
'Mafter of the Rolls-Office in *Philadelphia*.

'FOR all which this fhall be to you our fufficient Warrant, Commiffion and Au-
'thority.'

GIVEN under our Hands and Seals this Twenty-eighth Day of October, *One
Thoufand Seven Hundred and Fifty-one.*

THOMAS PENN, *L. S.*
RICHARD PENN, *L. S.*

Signed, fealed and delivered by the before named
THOMAS PENN, *and* RICHARD PENN,
Efquires, in the Prefence of us,
FRANCIS EYRE,
ROBERT GWYNN,

R E M A R K S.

THE *Defign of the Hofpital being (in itfelf) fo beneficent, and our honourable Proprietaries having fully exprefs'd their Approbation of it in ftrong Terms, as well
as declared their kind Intentions of aiding and affifting it, by granting a valuable Tract of
Land, in a proper Place, for an Hofpital; all therefore that feems neceffary for us to
do, is to convince our honourable Proprietaries, that the Methods by which they have propofed to aid and affift the Hofpital, will by no Means anfwer thefe good Intentions, but
are really inconfiftent therewith.*

*WE muft then beg Leave to remark in the firft Place, with regard to the Charter,
That as the Act of Affembly is undoubtedly the beft Grant of Incorporation that we can
poffibly have, and as the Reprefentatives of the Freemen of this Province have generoufly
contributed towards the Defign, we fhould fail of the Refpect that is juftly due to them,
were we to accept of any other, without obtaining fome very great and manifeft Advantage by it; but that there are no fuch Advantages in the Charter propofed, is evident at
firft View: On the contrary, we fhould by it be confined to ftricter Limits than we now
are, particularly with refpect to the Power of making By-Laws, and being fubjected to
Vifitors of the Proprietaries Appointment. But that Claufe which makes the Lot (and
of Confequence the Buildings on it) revert to the Proprietaries, on Failure of a Succeffion
of Contributors, is fo weighty an Objection, that were there no other, we could not en-*
tertain

tertain the leaſt Thoughts of accepting the Charter; for as the Sum allowed for Support of the Hoſpital is limited, we may reaſonably conclude, that in Time there will ceaſe to be a Succeſſion of Contributors, and no Perſon can imagine that when that happens to be the Caſe, the Lot and Buildings ought to become the private Property of any Man: And tho' the Act of Aſſembly hath made Proviſion in a Manner which may be liable to ſome Inconveniences, yet it can ſcarce fail of anſwering the Purpoſes firſt intended. The Proprietaries, to be ſure, have not attended to theſe Conſequences, or they never would have propoſed any Thing ſo inconſiſtent with the Deſign they intended to promote.

AS to the Lot that the Proprietaries deſigned for the Hoſpital, it is ſo ſituated, and ſo circumſtanced, that it will by no Means be ſuitable for the Purpoſe; it is a moiſt Piece of Ground, adjoining to the Brick-yards, where there are Ponds of ſtanding Water, and therefore muſt be unhealthy, and more fit for a Burying-place (to which Uſe Part of it is already applied) than for any other Service; beſides, as it is Part of a Square allotted by the late honourable Proprietary for publick Uſes, as the old Maps of the City will ſhew, our Fellow-citizens would tax us with Injuſtice to them, if we ſhould accept of this Lot by a Grant from our preſent Proprietaries, in ſuch Terms as would ſeem to imply our aſſenting to their having a Right to the Remainder of the Square.

Eſteemed Friends, Thomas Hyam,   *Philadelphia,* 2d of 7th Mo. 1752.
and Sylvanus Bevan,

' WE now, on Behalf of the Contributors to the *Pennſylvania* Hoſpital, with
'   much Gratitude and Reſpect, acknowledge the benevolent Diſpoſition you
' have manifeſted by your Induſtry and Care in ſolliciting our Addreſs to our Pro-
' prietaries; and as we are fully convinced nothing hath been wanting on your Parts,
' we ſhould have been much pleaſed that the Lot which the Proprietaries propoſed
' for the Hoſpital, and the Terms of their Grant, were ſuch as we deſired, or could
' accept.

' IMMEDIATELY after the Receipt of your Letter, with the Copy of that
' you had from the Proprietaries, our Preſident waited on the Governor, who was
' pleaſed to communicate to us the Inſtructions he had received; and as the An-
' ſwer given by the Proprietaries to you, may have induced you to think they had
' granted our Requeſt, we think it neceſſary to ſend you a Copy of their Inſtructions
' to the Governor, after Peruſal of which, and of the few Remarks we have made
' thereon, we have no Doubt you will approve of our Reſolutions not to accept of
' a Lot on theſe Terms.

' BEFORE we agreed on the Addreſs to the Proprietaries, we ſurvey'd the Square
' (of which the Lot propoſed by them is a Part) and the Situation appeared to us
' in every Reſpect inconvenient and unſuitable for our Purpoſe: It is contiguous to
' the Brick-makers Grounds, from which the City hath been furniſhed with Bricks
' above Forty Years paſt, ſo that their large Ponds being continually filled with
' ſtanding Water, renders the Neighbourhood unhealthy, and of courſe abſolutely
' improper for our Purpoſe, which is to reſtore the Sick to Health; and the only
' proper Uſe of that Square will be for a Burying-ground, to which Service ſome
' Part of it hath been applied by a Grant from the Proprietaries; and the Diſſatis-
' faction which appeared, and ſtill ſubſiſts among our Fellow-citizens, on the Pro-
'   ' prietaries

' prietaries claiming a Right to make that Grant is fo great, that if there were no
' other Objection, we would not run the Rifque of encreafing it.

' W E ftill think that the Lot we firft mentioned is more fuitable for us than any
' other fo near the City, and of fo fmall Value, and we are not entirely without Hopes
' that the Proprietaries, who have fo fully declared their Approbation of our Defign,
' will ftill grant the fame to us ; we are affured, if they regard their own Intereft in the
' Affections of the People, or even attend to the Juftice of their concurring in the
' Promoting of every Scheme calculated for the Publick Utility of their Province,
' they will chearfully grant it to us : And if you fhould entertain the fame Senti-
' ments, we requeft you to renew your Sollicitations to them, and if you find them
' ftill unwilling to favour our Requeft, we fhould be pleafed to know whether they
' will fell it to us, or let it for ever on an annual Rent, and the Price or Rent they pro-
' pofe; for as the Number of Contributors ftill continues gradually encreafing, we fhall
' rather endeavour to purchafe a Lot in a proper Situation, than to build the Houfe in
' an inconvenient Place, or to accept of any Lot on fuch Terms as we know would
' give a general Diffatisfaction.

' O N E of the Contributors hath offered to give a Lot of Ground much larger than
' that we now afk, and in a very good Air, but being about a Mile out of Town, we
' are apprehenfive it will be inconvenient to the Phyficians, who, as they freely give
' their Attendance, fhould be fubjected to as little Difficulty as poffible.

' W E have, for the prefent, hired a Houfe tolerably convenient, into which we
' began to admit Patients about fix Months fince ; the Number fince received is
' Twenty-three, of which Twelve have been cured and difcharged, and Eleven are
' remaining ; and as the Benefits of this Inftitution become daily more attended to,
' we have not the leaft Doubt that the Minds of fuch who are bleffed with the Means,
' will gradually become the more freely difpofed to contribute towards this good
' Work, and that it will foon become of general Service to the People of this Pro-
' vince.

' T H E kind Manner in which you have chearfully engaged to ferve us, gives us
' Reafon to think you will approve of our writing to you with fo much Freedom,
' we fhall not therefore offer any Apology for it.'

We are your obliged Friends.

Signed by Order, and on Behalf of the Managers of the Pennfylvania *Hofpital,*

JOSHUA CROSBY, Prefident.

To the MANAGERS of the *Pennfylvania* Hofpital.

Refpected Friends,
------------ *W E attended your Proprietary,* THOMAS PENN, *Efquire, and prefented
to him your Remarks on the Grant of Land made by him and his Brother* RICHARD *to
your Society (dated the Eighth of* October, 1751*) and requefted inftead thereof that Spot
which*

which your Memorial mentioned, and desired might be granted for the intended Hospital; he perused the Remarks, and made Objections to them, alledging that the Ground which you desired was contiguous to that which they have offered, consequently no Difference in the Healthiness thereof. And as to the Remark against its reverting to the Proprietaries, he very readily declared nothing more was intended by the Clause in the Grant, than that provided the Scheme for the Establishment and Continuance of the Hospital should not succeed, either for want of the Sum proposed to be raised as a Fund, or through any other Cause, that then the Ground should revert, &c. but as to the Erections thereon, they should be at the Managers Disposal. We desired his Answer in Writing, but he refused the Giving it in that Manner, and added, the Governor should have the necessary Instructions on the Affair, unto whom you might apply concerning it. On the whole, he came to this Resolution, not to make any Alteration in what was before granted, nor to lett or sell the Spot of Ground you pitch upon; and therefore we are of Opinion, you should either accept the Proprietary's Offer, with the Clause relating to the reverting to them being explained, or else to fix on some other Piece of Ground. And if there is no other Objection than the small Distance of a Mile to the Place which one of the Contributors hath offered to give you, may not that be more fit for an Hospital or Infirmary, than to have it in the City, where infectious Diseases may be much more liable to spread. We observe, with Pleasure, the Success that hath attended the Beginning of the good Work you are engaged in, and hope it will go forward, and be happily compleated, and are, with hearty Salutes,

Your real Friends,

THOMAS HYAM,
SYLVANUS BEVAN.

Esteemed Friends, *Thomas Hyam*,   Pennsylvania Hospital, 30th 6th Mo. 1753.
    and *Sylvanus Bevan*,

WE have lately received your Favour of *Thirty-first* First Month last, with Duplicate of your former Letters to our President, and being sensible that you have sollicited our Address to the Proprietaries with all the Diligence and Care we could desire or expect, we gratefully acknowledge your Friendship, and think ourselves under the same Obligations we should have been if your kind Endeavours had obtained the desired Effect.

THE Accounts of the Affairs of the Hospital, and of its present State, will be laid before the Assembly at their next Meeting, and soon after published, of which we shall direct Duplicates to be sent you; and as you have interested yourselves in the Promotion of it, and we are convinced of your good Wishes for its Success, when we can give you a pleasing Account of its Advancement, shall take the Liberty of communicating the same, being, with real Respects,

Your obliged Friends.

Signed on Behalf of the Board of Managers,

JOSHUA CROSBY.

C

THE.

THE following Papers were publifhed in the *Pennfylvania Gazette*, of *Auguft* the eighth, and fifteenth, 1751, *viz.*

Poft obitum benefacta manent, æternaque Virtus
Non metuit, Stygiis nec rapiatur Aquis.

I was fick, and ye vifited me.   MATTH. XXV.

' AMONG all the innumerable Species of Animals which inhabit the Air,
' Earth and Water, fo exceedingly different in their Production, their Proper-
' ties, and the Manner of their Exiftence, and fo varied in Form, that even of the
' fame Kind, it can fcarce be faid there are two Individuals in all Refpects alike ; it
' is remarkable there are none within our Obfervation diftinguifhed from the reft by
' this Particular, that they are by Nature incapable of Difeafes. The old Poets,
' how extravagant foever in their Fictions, durft never offend fo far againft Nature
' and Probability, as even to feign fuch a Thing ; and therefore, tho' they made
' their *Achilles* invulnerable from Head to Foot, and clad him befide in impenetrable
' Armour, forg'd by the Immortals, they were obliged to leave one foft unguarded
' Place in his Heel, how fmall foever, for Deftruction to enter at.----But tho' every
' Animal that hath Life is liable to Death, Man, of all other Creatures, has the
' greateft Number of Difeafes to his Share ; whether they are the Effects of our In-
' temperance and Vice, or are given us, that we may have a greater Opportunity of
' exercifing towards each other that Virtue, which moft of all recommends us to
' the Deity, I mean CHARITY.
' THE great Author of our Faith, whofe Life fhould be the conftant Object of
' our Imitation, as far as it is not inimitable, always fhew'd the greateft Compaffion
' and Regard for the Sick ; he difdain'd not to vifit and adminifter Comfort and
' Health to the meaneft of the People ; and he frequently inculcated the fame Dif-
' pofition in his Doctrine and Precepts to his Difciples. For this one Thing (in that
' beautiful Parable of the Traveller wounded by Thieves) the *Samaritan* (who was
' efteemed no better than a Heretick or Infidel by the Orthodox of thofe Times)
' is preferred to the Prieft and the *Levite*, becaufe he did not, like them, pafs by re-
' gardlefs of the Diftrefs of his Brother Mortal, but when he came to the Place
' where the half-dead Traveller lay, *he had Compaffion on him, and went to him, and*
' *bound up his Wounds, pouring in Oil and Wine, and fet him on his own Beaft, and*
' *brought him to an Inn, and took Care of him.*---*Dives*, alfo, the rich Man, is repre-
' fented as being excluded from the Happinefs of Heaven, becaufe he fared fump-
' tuoufly every Day, and had Plenty of all Things, and yet neglected to comfort
' and affift his poor Neighbour, who was helplefs, and *full of Sores*, and might
' perhaps have been revived and reftored with fmall Care, *by the Crumbs that fell*
' *from his Table*, or, as we fay, *with his loofe Corns.*---*I was fick, and ye vifited me*, is
' one of the Terms of Admiffion into Blifs, and the Contrary, a Caufe of Exclufion :
' That is, as our Saviour himfelf explains it, *Ye have vifited, or ye have not vifited,*
' *affifted and comforted thofe who ftood in need of it, even tho' they were the leaft, or*
' *meaneft of Mankind.* This Branch of Charity feems effential to the true Spirit of
                                                                    ' Chriftianity,

' Chriſtianity, and ſhould be extended to all in General, whether Deſerving or Un-
' deſerving, as far as our Power reaches. Of the ten Lepers who were cleanſed,
' nine ſeem to have been much more unworthy than the Tenth, yet, in reſpect to the
' Cure of their Diſeaſe, they equally ſhared the Goodneſs of G O D. And the
' great Phyſician in ſending forth his Diſciples, always gave them a particular Charge,
' *that into whatſoever City they entered, they ſhould heal all the Sick*, without Diſtinc-
' tion.

' W H E N the good *Samaritan* left his Patient at the Inn, *he gave Money to the
' Hoſt, and ſaid, take Care of him, and what thou ſpendeſt more, I will repay thee*. We
' are in this World mutual Hoſts to each other ; the Circumſtances and Fortunes of
' Men and Families are continually changing ; in the Courſe of a few Years we have
' ſeen the Rich become Poor, and the Poor Rich ; the Children of the Wealthy lan-
' guiſhing in Want and Miſery, and thoſe of their Servants lifted into Eſtates, and
' abounding in the good Things of this Life. Since then our preſent State, how
' proſperous ſoever, hath no Stability, but what depends on the good Providence of
' G O D, how careful ſhould we be not to harden our Hearts againſt the Diſtreſſes of
' our Fellow Creatures, leſt he who owns and governs All, ſhould puniſh our Inhu-
' manity, deprive us of a Stewardſhip in which we have ſo unworthily behaved,
' *laugh at our Calamity, and mock when our Fear cometh*. Methinks when Objects of
' Charity, and Opportunities of relieving them, preſent themſelves, we ſhould hear
' the Voice of this *Samaritan*, as if it were the Voice of G O D ſounding in our Ears,
' *Take Care of them, and whatſoever thou ſpendeſt, I will repay thee*.

' B U T the Good particular Men may do ſeparately in relieving the Sick, is ſmall,
' compared with what they may do collectively, or by a joint Endeavour and Intereſt.
' Hence the Erecting of Hoſpitals or Infirmaries by Subſcription, for the Reception,
' Entertainment, and Cure of the Sick Poor, has been found by Experience exceed-
' ingly beneficial, as they turn out annually great Numbers of Patients perfectly
' cured, who might otherwiſe have been loſt to their Families, and to Society.
' Hence Infirmaries ſpread more and more in *Europe*, new Ones being continually
' erected in large Cities and populous Towns, where generally the moſt ſkilful Phy-
' ſicians and Surgeons inhabit. And the Subſcribers have had the Satisfaction in a
' few Years of ſeeing the Good they propoſed to do, become much more extenſive
' than was at firſt expected ; for the Multitude and Variety of Caſes continually
' treated in thoſe Infirmaries, not only render the Phyſicians and Surgeons who at-
' tend them, ſtill more expert and ſkilful, for the Benefit of others, but afford ſuch
' ſpeedy and effectual Inſtruction to the young Students of both Profeſſions, who
' come from different and remote Parts of the Country for Improvement, that they
' return with a more ample Stock of Knowledge in their Art, and become Bleſſings
' to the Neighbourhoods in which they fix their Reſidence.

' I T is therefore a great Pleaſure to all the Benevolent and Charitable, who have
' been acquainted with theſe Things in other Countries, to obſerve, that an Inſtitu-
' tion of the ſame Kind has met with ſuch Encouragement in *Pennſylvania*, and is in
' ſuch Forwardneſs, that there is Reaſon to expect it may be carried into Execution
' the enſuing Year. May the Father of Mercies grant it his Bleſſing, and Thouſands
' of our unhappy Fellow Creatures, yet unborn, will have cauſe to bleſs him, for put-

' ting

' ting it into the Hearts of the generous Contributors, and enabling them thus to pro-
' vide for their Relief.'

Homines ad Deos, nulla re propius accedunt, quam Salutem Hominibus. dando.

CICER. ORAT.

' THIS Motto, taken from a Pagan Author, expreſſes the general Senſe of
' Mankind, even in the earlieſt Ages, concerning that great Duty and exten-
' ſive Charity, the adminiſtring Comfort and Relief to the Sick. If Men, withouf
' any other Aſſiſtance than the Dictates of natural Reaſon, had ſo high an Opinion
' of it, what may be expected from Chriſtians, to whom it has been ſo warmly re-
' commended by the beſt Example of human Conduct. To viſit the Sick, to feed
' the Hungry, to clothe the Naked, and comfort the Afflicted, are the inſeparable
' Duties of a Chriſtian Life.

' ACCORDINGLY 'tis obſervable, that the Chriſtian Doctrine hath had a real
' Effect on the Conduct of Mankind, which the mere Knowledge of Duty, without
' the Sanctions Revelation affords, never produced among the Heathens : For Hi-
' ſtory ſhows, that from the earlieſt Times of Chriſtianity, in all well regulated
' States where Chriſtians obtained ſufficient Influence, publick Funds and private
' Charities have been appropriated to the Building of Hoſpitals, for receiving, ſup-
' porting, and curing thoſe unhappy Creatures, whoſe Poverty is aggravated by the
' additional Load of bodily Pain. But of theſe Kind of Inſtitutions among the
' Pagans, there is no Trace in the Hiſtory of their Times.

' THAT good Prince EDWARD VI. was ſo affected at the Miſeries of his poor
' diſeaſed Subjects, repreſented in a Charity Sermon preach'd to him on the Occa-
' ſion, that he ſoon after laid the Foundation of four of the largeſt Hoſpitals now
' in *London*, which the Citizens finiſhed, and have ever ſince maintain'd.

' IN *Hide-park*, at *Bath*, in *Edinburgh*, *Liverpool*, *Winchester*, and in the County
' of *Devon*, and ſundry other Places in *Great-Britain*, large and commodious In-
' firmaries have been lately erected, from trifling Beginnings of private Charities :
' And ſo wonderfully does Providence favour theſe pious Inſtitutions, that there is
' not an Inſtance of any One's failing for want of neceſſary charitable Contributions. *

THE

* *Extract from the* Tour through Great-Britain, *Vol.* 3. *Page* 293.

' IN the Year 1740, on the Promotion of Dr. *Gilbert*, Dean of this Church, to the Biſhoprick of
' *Landaff*, his Majeſty was pleaſed to confer the Deanery on Dr. *Alured Clarke*, who was inſtalled in
' the Month of *January*, in that Year ; and if we may be allowed to judge from the pious Acts he
' began with in that Station, a more worthy Man could not have been preferr'd thereto.

' THE Houſe, an ancient Building, belonging to that Dignity, had, thro' the Remiſſneſs of its
' former Poſſeſſors, been too long neglected ; wherefore his firſt Work was to ſet about altering and
' repairing that, which he did within nine Months of his Inſtalment, at an Expence of about *Eight*
' *Hundred Pounds.*

' BEFORE this was perfected, *viz.* in the Spring 1741, he drew up and publiſhed Propoſals for found-
' ing an Hoſpital in this City, for lodging, dieting, and curing the ſick and lame Poor thereof, and of
' the County of *Devon*, on the like Plan of that which he had before founded at *Winchester*, for the
' Benefit of that City, and County of *Hants*. A Deſign ſo good, recommended by the pious Elo-
' quence of a Divine ſo learned and judicious, on Views ſo viſibly diſintereſted, and ſo clearly ab-

' ſtracted

' THE Increase of poor diseased Foreigners and others, settled in the distant Parts
' of this Province, where regular Advice and Assistance cannot be procured, but at
' an Expence that neither they nor their Townships can afford, has waken'd the At-
' tention of sundry humane and well disposed Minds, to procure some more certain,
' effectual and easy Methods for their Relief than have hitherto been provided; and
' having represented the Affair to the Assembly, a Law was passed, without one
' dissenting Voice, giving *Two Thousand Pounds* for building and furnishing a Pro-
' vincial Hospital, on Condition that *Two Thousand Pounds* more should be raised
' by private Donations, to be put out to Interest as Part of a perpetual Fund for
' supporting it; and the Contributors were made a Body Corporate, with all the Pow-
' ers necessary on the Occasion. Since which, People of all Ranks in this City have
' united zealously and heartily in promoting this pious and excellent Design, and
' more than the Sum stipulated was subscribed in a few Days only, and a much larger
' Sum will probably be raised here, if the Country chearfully contributes to the Capi-
· tal Stock, which 'tis not to be doubted they will do, when they consider how
' much they are interested in it.

' THE Difference between nursing and curing the Sick in an Hospital, and sepa-
' rately in private Lodgings, with Regard to the Expence, is at least as ten to one.
' For Instance, suppose a Person under the Necessity of having a Limb amputated,
' he must have the constant Attendance of a Nurse, a Room, Fire, &c. which can-
' not for the first three or four Weeks be procured at less Expence than *Fifteen Shil-*
' *lings* a Week, and never after at less than *Ten*: If he continues two Months, his
· Nursing will be *Five Pounds*, his Surgeon's Fee, and other accidental Charges,
' commonly amounts to *Three Pounds*, in the whole near *Ten Pounds*; whereas in an
' Hospital, one Nurse, one Fire, &c. will be sufficient for ten Patients, the Extra
' Expences will be inconsiderable, and the Surgeons Fees taken off, which will bring
' the above Calculation within the Limits of Truth.

' BUT the Difference with regard to the unhappy Sufferer is still greater. In an
' Hospital his Case will be treated according to the best Rules of Art, by Men of
' Experience and known Abilities in their Profession. His Lodgings will be com-
' modious, clean and neat, in an healthy and open Situation, his Diet will be well
' chosen, and properly administred: He will have many other necessary Convenien-

' ces

' stracted from all Party Schemes or Intentions, met with the general Applause and Assistance of the
' Gentry and Clergy of all Parties, Sects and Denominations; who, however different in Religion
' and Politicks, unanimously join'd in this pious Undertaking: And a Subscription being opened in
' *March*, hath already (*November,* 1741) brought in about *Two Thousand Pounds*, of which near *Fif-*
' *teen Hundred Pounds* are annual Engagements, which, 'tis highly probable, will be not only conti-
' nued, but much augmented, so that 'tis hoped that Two Hundred Patients at a Time may be pro-
' vided for. *John Tuckfield*, of *Raddon*, Esq; was pleased to accommodate the Governors with a Plot
' of Ground near *Southernhay*, without the City Walls, at a very moderate Price, and to give *One*
' *Hundred Pounds* towards carrying on the Building for the intended Hospital, the Plan of which was
' commodiously designed by the Direction of the Dean, and the first Stone thereof laid by him, assisted
' by the Bishop of *Exon*, Sir *William Courtenay*, Knight of the Shire, Sir *Henry Northcote*, and *Hum-*
' *phry Sydenham*, Esquires, the Citizens in Parliament, the Honourable *Henry Rolle*, and *John Tuck-*
' *field*, Esq; attended by a great Number of Clergy and Gentry, that are Subscribers, and Thousands
' of joyful Spectators, on the Twenty-seventh of *August,* 1741. The Building contains upwards of
' Three Hundred Feet in Length, and is already in a good Forwardness.

' ces for his Relief, such as hot and cold Baths, Sweating-rooms, Chirurgic Ma-
' chines, Bandage, &c. which can rarely be procured in the best private Lodgings,
' much less in those miserable loathsome Holes, which are the common Receptacles
' of the diseased Poor that are brought to this City.----In short, a Beggar, in a well
' regulated Hospital, stands an equal Chance with a Prince in his Palace for a com-
' fortable Subsistence, and an expeditious and effectual Cure of his Diseases.

' I T is hoped therefore, that whoever will maturely consider the inestimable
' Blessings that are connected to a proper Execution of the present Hospital Scheme
' in this City, can never be so void of Humanity, and the essential Duties of Re-
' ligion, as to turn a deaf Ear to the numberless Cries of the Poor and Needy, and
' refuse, for their Assistance, a little of that Superfluity, which a bountiful Provi-
' dence has so liberally bestowed on them.'

O N the Sixteenth of *August* it being made appear, to the Satisfaction of the Assembly, that the Contributions amounted to upwards of *Two Thousand Pounds*, an Order
was obtained for the *Two Thousand Pounds* that had been conditionally granted by the
Act, *One Thousand Pounds* to be paid immediately, the other in Twelve Months:
The Money, when received, was lett out at Interest on good Security, that it might
be improving till it should be wanted for the Building, which the Managers were
obliged to postpone till a Piece of Ground could be obtained that would afford sufficient Room in an airy, healthy Situation, and yet so nigh the built Streets of the
City, as that the Managers, Physicians and Surgeons, might readily and conveniently
visit the House on every Occasion. But that some Good might be doing in the
mean Time, the Managers concluded to hire a House, and take in some Patients for a
Beginning; but some Doubts arising concerning the Power and Duty of the Managers,
a general Meeting of the Contributors was called to settle the same, and the following
Law was passed for those and other Purposes, *viz.*

A LAW for regulating the Elections of the Managers and Treasurer of the Pennsylvania *Hospital, and declaring their Trust, Duty and Authority.*

' WHEREAS by an Act of the General Assembly of the Province of *Penn-*
' *sylvania*, intituled, *An Act to encourage the Establishing of an Hospital for*
' *the Relief of the Sick Poor of this Province, and for the Reception and*
' *Cure of Lunaticks*, the Contributors to the said Hospital are made a Body Corpo-
' rate, and impowered to meet, and to make such Laws, Rules and Orders, as
' shall appear to them the said Contributors met, or the major Part of them, to be
' good, useful and necessary, for the well governing and regulating the said Hospital,
' and for the Regulation of the Elections of Managers, a Treasurer, and other ne-
' cessary Officers and Ministers thereof, and for limiting and appointing their Num-
' ber, Trust and Authority.

' A N D whereas, in Pursuance of the said Law, the Contributors have met, and
' have chosen twelve Managers and a Treasurer, which Treasurer hath received con-
' siderable Sums of Money for the Use of the said Hospital, and it is now become
' necessary, for the more orderly Disposition and Application of the said Monies, and
' of

' of such Sums as may hereafter be received, and for the more sure Direction of the
' Managers and Treasurer therein, to declare and appoint their Trust, Authority
' and Duty : Therefore it is enacted by the Contributors to the *Pennsylvania* Hospi-
' tal, in general Meeting duly assembled, That the Managers of the said Hospital
' for the Time being, shall have the Power of disposing of all Monies paid to the
' Treasurer for the Building, Furnishing, Support, Use and Service of the Hospi-
' tal, and for the Hiring and Furnishing a House or Houses for the Reception of
' Patients, until the said Hospital shall be built, under the Limitations and Restric-
' tions of the before-mentioned Act of Assembly. And the said Managers shall
' likewise have the Power to direct the Manner and Terms of receiving and dis-
' charging of Patients ; and all Officers and Servants belonging to the Hospital,
' other than the Treasurer, shall be in the Choice, and under the Direction of the
' Managers, who shall allow and order their respective Salaries, and may displace
' them, and appoint others, as often as they shall think fit. And the said Managers
' shall have the Power of calling general Meetings of the Contributors, as often as
' they judge it necessary for the Service and Advantage of the Hospital ; and shall
' cause due and publick Notice to be given of the Time, Place, and Design or
' Purpose of such occasional Meeting, at least ten Days before the same is to be held,
' and shall nominate some discreet Member to preside therein, and regulate the De-
' bates thereof. And the said Managers shall have the Keeping, and Power of af-
' fixing, the Seal of the Corporation, which Seal shall be made nearly agreeable to the
' Form or Draught hereunto annexed ; and they shall settle the Accounts with the
' Treasurer from Time to Time, and take Care that all Laws, Rules and Orders
' made by the Contributors, and legally approved, be duly and faithfully executed ;
' for all which, or any other Services relating to the Hospital, they shall not claim,
' receive, or retain, any Fee, Gratuity or Reward whatsoever.

' A N D for the more orderly Execution of their Duty and Trust, the Managers
' are hereby required to meet at least once a Month at the Hospital, or some other
' fit Place in the City of *Philadelphia,* to confer and conclude concerning the Mat-
' ters hereby committed to them ; and shall cause fair Minutes of their Proceedings
' to be kept by their Clerk, in a Book to be provided for that Purpose : In every
' of which Meetings of the Managers aforesaid, eight of their Number met shall
' be a Quorum, capable to consult, confer and conclude of and upon all Matters
' appertaining to their Trust, according to the aforesaid Act of Assembly, and the
' Laws of this Corporation ; and whatsoever seven of the Number so met shall so
' conclude, shall be deemed and taken for and as the Resolution of the Managers
' for the Time, and accordingly enter'd in their Minutes. To which Minutes, and
' also to the Treasurer's Accounts, all Persons concerned shall have free Recourse at
' all seasonable Times.

' A N D it is further enacted by the Contributors aforesaid, that every Treasurer
' hereafter chosen shall, before he take upon himself the Execution of his Office, en-
' ter into an Obligation, with one sufficient Surety, in double the Value that doth, or
' probably may come into his Hands, during the Continuance of his Office, as near
' as can be estimated by the Managers, unto the Contributors of the *Pennsylvania*
' Hospital ; conditioned, that he will, once in three Months, or oftener if required,
' render

' render his Accounts to the Managers of the said Hospital, and well and truly ac-
' count, adjust and settle with them when required, for and concerning all Monies
' that are or shall come into his Hands belonging to the said Contributors, and pay
' the Ballance that shall appear on such Settlement to be in his Hands, unto such
' Person, or for such Service as a Board of Managers for the Time being shall or-
' der and appoint, and not otherwise ; and that he will at the Expiration of his Of-
' fice, well and truly deliver up and pay the Ballance of the Monies then remaining
' in his Hands, together with the Books of Accounts concerning the same, and
' other the Papers and Writings in his Keeping belonging to the Contributors,
' unto his Successor in the said Office ; and that he will do and execute all other
' Things as Treasurer to the Contributors aforesaid, according to the true Sense and
' Meaning of this Law. And he is hereby authorised immediately upon entring into
' his Office, to demand and receive of the preceding Treasurer, his Heirs, Execu-
' tors or Administrators, the Cash, Books of Accounts, Writings and other Effects
' belonging to the Corporation, giving his Receipt for the same.

AND for the more regular and satisfactory conducting of future Elections, and
' the Preventing of Disputes and Misunderstandings among the Contributors, con-
' cerning the same, it is hereby farther enacted, That the Place and Hour of the
' Election shall be appointed by the Managers of the current Year, and notified by
' their Clerk, at least twenty Days before the Election, by printed Advertisements :
' And the said Managers shall and are hereby required and impowered to nominate
' three discreet Members of this Corporation to inspect and judge of the said Election,
' and declare who are the Persons elected ; and the Managers shall cause their Clerk
' to enter in their Book of Minutes the Names of the Persons elected, according
' to the Tickets.

' AND if any Person elected Manager, shall refuse or neglect to act, or shall be
' absent from three successive Monthly Meetings of the Managers, in any of the first
' ten Months of the Year for which he shall be elected Manager ; or if within the
' same Year or Term of his Office, he shall be confined by Sickness, or otherwise
' render'd incapable of executing the Office of a Manager, according to the true
' Meaning of this Law, or shall die, the rest of the Managers, as often as Occasion
' shall require, in any of the Cases aforesaid, shall proceed in their Duty and Office
' without him ; or if they think fit they shall nominate another of the Contributors
' to supply his Place of a Manager until the then next ensuing Election.

' AND if any Person so elected Treasurer, shall absent himself from his said Of-
' fice for the Space of thirty Days, or shall be otherwise render'd incapable, or ne-
' glect his Office or Duty of Treasurer, it shall and may be lawful for the Mana-
' gers for the Time being, to displace him from the said Office ; and the Managers
' causing their Clerk to make a Minute for the Purpose, containing their Reasons
' for displacing him, he shall thereupon, and from thenceforth, cease to be the
' Treasurer aforesaid, and shall, upon Notice thereof, adjust and settle with the
' Managers, and pay and deliver the Money, Books, Writings, Accounts, and all
' other Effects whatsoever in his Hands belonging to this Corporation, to such
' Person or Persons as the Managers shall order and appoint ; and in that Case, and
' so often, and also if the Treasurer shall depart this Life, the Managers shall no-
' minate

'minate another of the Members of this Corporation, but not of their own Num-
'ber, to be Treafurer until the next Meeting for the annual Election, or other ge-
'neral Meeting of the Contributors.

' P R O V I D E D always, any Thing herein contained to the contrary notwithftand-
'ing, That before the Managers for the Time being proceed to erect any Building
'for the faid Hofpital, a Plan of fuch propofed Building, with an Eftimation of the
'Expence, fhall be prepared and laid before a general Meeting of the Contributors
'for their Confideration ; and their Approbation fhall be obtained before the fame
'is carried into Execution.'

Signed by Order of a general Meeting of the Contributors,

Joshua Crosby, Prefident.

January 17, 1752, *The above Bill was read*
three Times at a general Meeting of the Con-
tributors to the Pennfylvania *Hofpital, and*
pafs'd by a very great Majority.

B. Franklin, Clerk.

We approve this Law,   William Allen, Chief Juftice.
Isaac Norris, Speaker of the Affembly.
Tench Francis, Attorney General.

The Managers hired the moft convenient Houfe that could be procured, with
Gardens, &c. agreed with a Matron to govern the Family, and nurfe the Sick, and
provided Beds and other neceffary Furniture ; and prepared the following Rules re-
fpecting the Admiffion and Difcharge of Patients, a Number of which were printed
and difperfed among the Contributors, *viz.*

R U L E S agreed to by the Managers *of the* Pennfylvania *Hofpital, for the Ad-*
miffion and Difcharge of Patients.

' *Firft,* T H A T no Patients fhall be admitted whofe Cafes are judg'd incurable,
'   Lunaticks excepted ; nor any whofe Cafes do not require the particular
'Conveniences of an Hofpital.

' *Secondly,* T H A T no Perfon, having the Small-pox, Itch, or other infectious
'Diftempers, fhall be admitted, until there are proper Apartments prepared for the
'Reception of fuch as are afflicted with thofe Difeafes ; and if any fuch Perfons
'fhould be inadvertently admitted, they fhall forthwith be difcharged.

' *Thirdly,* T H A T Women having young Children fhall not be received, unlefs
'their Children are taken Care of elfewhere, that the Hofpital may not be burthen'd
'with the Maintenance of fuch Children, nor the Patients difturbed with their Noife.

' *Fourthly,* T H A T all Perfons defirous of being admitted into the Hofpital (not
'Inhabitants of *Philadelphia*) muft, before they leave their Abode, have their Cafes
'drawn up in a plain Manner, and fent to the Managers, together with a Certificate
'from a Juftice of Peace, and the Overfeer or Overfeers of the Poor of the Town-

D   'fhip

‘ ſhip in which they reſide, that they have gain’d a Reſidence in ſuch Townſhip,
‘ and are unable to pay for Medicines and Attendance; to which an Anſwer ſhall
‘ ſpeedily be returned, informing them whether and when they may be admitted.
‘ All Perſons employed in drawing up their Caſes, are deſired to be particular in
‘ enumerating the Symptoms, and to mention the Patient’s Age, Sex, and Place of
‘ Abode, with the Diſtance from the City of *Philadelphia.*

‘ *Fifthly,* THAT all Perſons who have thus obtained a Letter of Licence to be
‘ received into the Hoſpital, muſt be there at the Time mentioned for their Re-
‘ ception, and bring with them that Letter, and muſt likewiſe depoſite in the Hands
‘ of the Treaſurer ſo much Money, or give ſuch Security as ſhall be mentioned in
‘ their reſpective Letters of Licence, to indemnify the Hoſpital either from the Ex-
‘ pence of Burial, in caſe they die, or to defray the Expence of carrying them
‘ back to their Place of Abode, and that they may not become a Charge to the
‘ City.

‘ *Sixthly,* IF ſeveral Perſons, not excluded by the preceding Exceptions, are ap-
‘ plying when they cannot be received, without exceeding the Number allowed by
‘ the Managers to be entertained at one Time in the Hoſpital, the Preference will be
‘ given, when the Caſes are equally urgent, firſt to ſuch as are recommended by one
‘ or more of the Contributors, Members of this Corporation, reſiding in the Town-
‘ ſhip to which the poor Perſons belong ; ſecondly, to thoſe who ſtand firſt in the
‘ Liſt of Applications ; but if ſome Caſes are urgent, and others can admit of Delay,
‘ thoſe with the moſt urgent Symptoms ſhall be preferred.

‘ *Seventhly,* NOTWITHSTANDING ſuch Letters of Licence, if it ſhall ap-
‘ pear by a perſonal Examination of any of the Patients, that their Caſes are miſ-
‘ repreſented, and that they are improper Subjects of the Hoſpital, the Managers
‘ ſhall have the Power of refuſing them Admiſſion.

‘ *Eighthly,* THAT at leaſt one Bed ſhall be provided for Accidents that require
‘ immediate Relief.

‘ *Ninthly,* THAT if there ſhall be Room in the Hoſpital to ſpare, after as many
‘ poor Patients are accommodated as the Intereſt of the Capital Stock can ſup-
‘ port, the Managers ſhall have the Liberty of taking in other Patients, at ſuch rea-
‘ ſonable Rates as they can agree for ; and the Profits ariſing from boarding and
‘ nurſing ſuch Patients, ſhall be appropriated to the ſame Uſes as the Intereſt-money
‘ of the publick Stock. Provided that no ſuch Perſons, under Pretence of coming
‘ to board in the Hoſpital, ſhall be admitted, unleſs, on the firſt Application
‘ made on his Behalf, a Certificate be produced from the Overſeer or Overſeers of
‘ the Poor of the Townſhip in which he lives, of his having gained a Reſidence in the
‘ ſaid Townſhip ; and unleſs ſufficient Security be given to the Managers to indem-
‘ nify the City and Hoſpital from all Charges and Expences whatſoever, occaſioned
‘ by his removing hither.

‘ *Tenthly,* THAT thoſe who are taken into the Hoſpital at a private Expence,
‘ may employ any Phyſicians or Surgeons they deſire.

‘ *Eleventhly,* THAT all Perſons who have been admitted into the Hoſpital, ſhall
‘ be diſcharged as ſoon as they are cured, or, after a reaſonable Time of Trial,
‘ are judg’d incurable. *Twelfthly,*

' *Twelfthly*, THAT all Patients when cured, fign Certificates of their particular
' Cafes, and of the Benefit they have received in this Hofpital, to be either pub-
' lifhed or otherwife difpofed of, as the Managers may think proper.

' *Thirteenthly*, THAT no Patient go out of the Hofpital without Leave from one
' of the Phyficians or Surgeons firft fignified to the Matron : That they do not
' fwear, curfe, get drunk, behave rudely or indecently, on Pain of Expulfion after
' the firft Admonition.

' *Fourteenthly*, THAT no Patient prefume to play at Cards, Dice, or any other
' Game within the Hofpital, or to beg any where in the City of *Philadelphia*, on
' Pain of being difcharged for Irregularity.

' *Fifteenthly*, THAT fuch Patients as are able fhall affift in nurfing others, wafh-
' ing and ironing the Linen, wafhing and cleaning the Rooms, and fuch other Ser-
' vices as the Matron fhall require.'

THE foregoing Rules were agreed to by a Board of Managers of the Pennfylvania
Hofpital, the Twenty-third Day of the Firft Month (January) 1752.

BENJAMIN FRANKLIN, Clerk.

We do approve of the foregoing Rules,   WILLIAM ALLEN, Chief Juftice.
ISAAC NORRIS, Speaker of the Affembly.
TENCH FRANCIS, Attorney General.

ABOUT this Time all the Phyficians and Surgeons, who were Contributors,
were confulted, in order to form fome Rules relating to the Choice, Admiffion and
Conduct of the Practitioners, and, after fundry Meetings, the following were prepared and agreed to at a general Meeting of the Contributors, *viz.*

RULES to be obferved in the Choice of the Phyficians and Surgeons of the Pennfylvania *Hofpital*, to limit and appoint their Number, Authority and Duty, and to
raife a Fund for fupplying the faid Hofpital with Medicines.

' *Imprimis*, THE Managers of the faid Hofpital fhall, within ten Days after
'   their firft Meeting in the Month called *May*, yearly, choofe fix
' Practitioners in Phyfick and Surgery, to vifit and take Care of the Patients in the
' faid Hofpital, and the other Practitioners (who are at this Time Members of this
' Corporation) fhall have the Privilege of attending and obferving the Practice of
' thofe chofen for the Service of the Year.

' *Secondly*, THE Practitioners chofen fhall give their Attendance at fuch Times,
' and in fuch Manner, and be claffed with each other, as fhall be concluded and
' agreed upon by the Managers and Practitioners.

' *Thirdly*, UPON extraordinary Cafes, the Practitioners in Attendance fhall call in
' two or more of the Practitioners chofen for the Service of the Year, to confult
' with.

' *Fourthly*, IN all fuch Cafes, which will admit of Time for Deliberation, all the fix
' Practitioners chofen for the Service of the Year, fhall have timely Notice thereof.

D 2   ' *Fifthly*,

' *Fifthly*, IF any Practitioner be removed by the Managers for Neglect of Duty,
' or any other Caufe, or fhall die, in that Cafe the Managers fhall choofe another
' Practitioner (who is a Member of this Corporation) to fupply his Place.

' *Sixthly*, EACH Apprentice or other Student the Practitioners fhall introduce
' to fee the Practice of the Hofpital, fhall pay one *Englifh Guinea*, or *Thirty-four*
' *Shillings*, current Money, *per* Year, to be laid out in Medicines, or fuch other
' Manner as the Managers think moft proper.

' *Seventhly*, No Practitioner, during the Term for which he is chofen to ferve
' the Hofpital, fhall act as a Manager.

' *Eighthly*, THE Practitioners fhall keep a fair Account (in a Book provided
' for that Purpofe) of the feveral Patients under their Care, of the Diforders
' they labour under, and fhall enter in the faid Book the Recipes or Prefcriptions
' they make for each of them.

' *Ninthly*, No Perfon fhall be received hereafter as a Candidate to be employed in
' the faid Hofpital, as a Phyfician or Surgeon, until he be a Member of this Cor-
' poration, and of the Age of Twenty-feven Years, hath ferv'd a regular Appren-
' ticefhip in this City or Suburbs, hath ftudied Phyfick or Surgery feven Years or
' more, and hath undergone an Examination of fix of the Practitioners of the Ho-
' fpital, in the Prefence of the Managers, and is approved of by them : And with
' refpect to Strangers, they fhall have refided three Years or more in this City, and
' fhall be examined and approved of in the Manner, and under the Reftrictions
' aforefaid.

' *Tenthly*, THESE Rules fhall continue in Force two Years, and from thence to
' the Time of the next general Meeting of the Contributors, and no longer.

*THE foregoing Rules were agreed to at a general Meeting of the Contributors to
the* Pennfylvania *Hofpital, the fixth Day of* April, 1752, *and three Times read,
and ordered to be engroffed ; and at a Meeting of the Contributors on the thirteenth
Day of* April, 1752, *were again read, and, by their Order, figned by*

JOSHUA CROSBY, Prefident.

We do approve of thefe Rules,　　WILLIAM ALLEN, Chief Juftice.
　　　　　　　　　　　　　　ISAAC NORRIS, Speaker of the Affembly:
　　　　　　　　　　　　　　TENCH FRANCIS, Attorney General.

THROUGH the Induftry of the Managers, every Thing was ready for the Admiffion of Patients by the Tenth of *February*, 1752, and the firft were accordingly
taken in on that Day. From which Time the Phyficians and Surgeons, with a Committee of the Managers, have conftantly and chearfully given Attendance at the
Houfe twice a Week, to vifit the Sick, examine Cafes, admit and difcharge Patients,
&c. befides the daily Attendance of the former.

ON

On the 7th of *May*, 1752, there was a new Choice of Directors, and a Treasurer, *viz.*

M A N A G E R S,

Joshua Crosby,	Isaac Jones,
Hugh Roberts,	Samuel Rhodes,
John Smith,	Samuel Hazard,
Israel Pemberton, jun.	John Reynell,
Benjamin Franklin,	William Griffitts,
Joseph Morris,	Thomas Lawrence, jun.

T R E A S U R E R, Charles Norris.

The Managers met soon after, and chose six Physicians and Surgeons for the ensuing Year, *viz.* Doctors *Lloyd Zachary, Thomas Bond, Phineas Bond, Thomas Cadwallader, Samuel Preston Moore,* and *John Redman*; and those agreed to attend in the following Order.

May	Lloyd Zachary	T. Cadwallader	Thomas Bond		
June		T. Cadwallader	Thomas Bond	S. Preston Moore	
July			Thomas Bond	S. Preston Moore	Phineas Bond
August				S. Preston Moore	Phineas Bond	John Redman
September	Lloyd Zachary				Phineas Bond	John Redman
October	Lloyd Zachary	T. Cadwallader				John Redman
November	Lloyd Zachary	T. Cadwallader	Thomas Bond		
December		T. Cadwallader	Thomas Bond	S. Preston Moore	
January			Thomas Bond	S. Preston Moore	Phineas Bond
February				S. Preston Moore	Phineas Bond	John Redman
March	Lloyd Zachary				Phineas Bond	John Redman
April	Lloyd Zachary	T. Cadwallader				John Redman

The Practitioners charitably supplied the Medicines *gratis* till *December*, 1752, when the Managers having procured an Assortment of Drugs from *London*, opened an Apothecary's Shop in the Hospital, and it being found necessary, appointed an Apothecary to attend and make up the Medicines daily, according to the Prescriptions, with an Allowance of *Fifteen Pounds per Annum* for his Care and Trouble, he giving Bond, with two sufficient Sureties, for the faithful Performance of his Trust. ---To pay for these Medicines, which cost *One Hundred Twelve Pounds, Fifteen Shillings,* and *Two-pence Halfpenny, Sterling,* a Subscription was set on Foot among
the

the charitable Widows, and other good Women of the City, and the following Sums were contributed, *viz.*

Mary Allen,	-	-	£ 24	6	0	Hannah Lloyd,	-	-	£ 3	0	0
Margaret Clymer,	-	-	1	7	0	Sarah Mifflin,	-	-	2	0	0
Deborah Claypoole,	-	-	5	8	0	Debby Morris,	-	-	2	14	0
Mary Calvert,	-	-	2	0	0	Debby Norris,	-	-	5	8	0
Susannah Dillwyn,	-	-	5	0	0	Content Nicholson,	-	-	1	0	0
Sarah Edgell,	-	-	3	0	0	Hannah Ogden,	-	-	2	0	0
Sarah Fishbourne,	-	-	2	0	0	Mary Plumstead,	-	-	1	14	6
Abigail Griffitts,	-	-	10	0	0	Mary Powell,	-	-	5	8	0
Frances Griffitts,	-	-	2	3	6	Elizabeth Paschall,	-	-	3	0	0
Elizabeth Griffitts, jun.	-	1	7	0	Beulah Paschall,	-	-	1	7	0
Elizabeth Holton,	-	-	1	0	0	Martha Roberts,	-	-	1	0	0
Hannah Kearney,	-	-	1	0	0	Mary Standley,	-	-	5	8	0
Miriam Kelly,	-	-	1	7	0	Ann Strettel,	-	-	2	0	0
Sarah Lloyd,	-	-	1	10	0	Rebecca Steel,	-	-	3	0	0
Sarah Logan,	-	-	10	0	0	Sundry Women, by *Isaac Jones*,	3	10	0

FROM this Bounty the Managers have since been enabled to furnish Medicines to many poor Out-patients, who, at their Request, have been kindly visited by the Physicians *gratis*, besides the Service of them to those in the Hospital.

ABOUT the Beginning of this Year twelve Tin Boxes were provided, on which were written these Words in Gold Letters, *CHARITY FOR THE HOSPITAL.* One Box for each Manager, to be put up in his House, ready to receive casual Benefactions, in Imitation of a good Custom practised in some foreign Countries, where these Kind of Boxes are frequent in Shops, Stores, and other Places of Business, and into which the Buyer and Seller (when different Prices are proposed) often agree to throw the Difference, instead of splitting it: In which the Successful in Trade sometimes piously deposite a Part of their extraordinary Gains, and Magistrates throw their petty Fees; a Custom worthy Imitation! But these Boxes among us have produced but little for the Hospital as yet, not through want of Charity in our People, but from their being unacquainted with the Nature and Design of them.

IN *March*, 1753, Doctor *Lloyd Zachary*, who had diligently attended the Hospital from the Beginning, being disabled by a paralytick Disorder, Doctor *William Shippen* was about this Time chosen, by the Managers, to supply his Place.

IN *May*, 1753, the Committee of Managers appointed to settle the Accounts of the Hospital, made a Report of them, of which the following is an Abstract, *viz.*

UPON

UPON a View of the general Accounts of the Hospital, from the Beginning to this Day, we find them to ftand as follows :

Dr. *The Stock given by Law for founding, building and furnifhing the Provincial Hospital.* **Cr.**

	£	s	d		£	s	d
To real Securities in the Treafurer's Hands for fundry Sums lent out on Intereft,	1850	0	0	By two Orders drawn by the Speaker of the Affembly upon the Truftees of the Loan-Office, and paid,	2000	0	0
To Houfe-rent and Furniture to this Date,	185	10	5	By fundry Sums received for Intereft of Money lent,	67	0	0
	£ 2035	10	5		£ 2067	0	0
Ballance due to the Stock,	31	9	7				
	£ 2067	0	0				

Dr. *The Capital Stock of the Provincial Hospital.* **Cr.**

	£	s	d		£	s	d
To fixty Bonds given by fundry Subfcribers, amounting to	1454	16	8	By One Hundred and Thirty-five Subfcriptions, amounting in the Whole to *Two Thoufand Seven Hundred and Fifty-one Pounds, Sixteen Shillings, and Eight pence,*	2751	16	8
To fundry Subfcriptions, for which Bonds are not yet given,	335	0	0				
To real Securities in the Treafurer's Hands, for fundry Sums lent out on Intereft,	800	0	0				
To an Annuity of *Thirty-five Shillings Sterling, per Annum,* iffuing out of a Lot of Land on *Cedar-ftreet,* given by *Jofeph Wharton,* in Lieu of his Subfcription,	50	0	0				
To a Lot of Land in the *Northern Liberties,* given by *Matthias Koplin,* as a Subfcription,	24	0	0				
	£ 2663	16	8				
Ballance due to Capital Stock,	88	0	0				
	£ 2751	16	8				

Dr. *The Maintenance of the* Pennfylvania *Hospital.* **Cr.**

	£	s	d		£	s	d
To Expences of Houfe-keeping, Fire-wood and Wages, from the Beginning to this Date, amounting to,	300	13	9¾	By Intereft-money received to this Date,	121	11	6
				By fundry Sums received for boarding Patients on Pay	80	11	4
				By a Donation from *B. Franklin*'s Charity-Box,	1	10	0
					£ 203	12	10
				Ball. expended more than received,	97	0	11¾
					£ 300	13	9¾

WE do alfo herewith lay before the Board, a compleat Lift of Subfcribers, and an Account of the Patients received in the Hofpital to this Time, by which it appears,

pears, That from the Eleventh of the *Second Month*, 1752, to the Fourth of the *Fifth Month*, 1753, there have been Sixty-four Patients received.

Of which 32 have been cured and difcharged.

4 have been confiderably relieved.

5 difcharged as Incurables.

1 difcharged for irregular Behaviour.

1 difcharged becaufe admitted contrary to Rules.

2 left the Hofpital without Leave.

6 have been taken away by their Friends.

5 have died with various Diforders.

8 remains.

In all, 64

W E likewife report, that feveral Out-patients have received the Advice of the Phyficians, and the Ufe of the Medicines, *&c.*

All which we fubmit to the Board,

Philadelphia, 5th Mo. 5, 1753.

SAMUEL HAZARD,
JOHN REYNELL,
JOHN SMITH.

T H E Managers and Treafurer chofen at the Election on the 7th of *May*, 1753, were as follows, *viz.*

M A N A G E R S,

JOSHUA CROSBY,	SAMUEL HAZARD,
BENJAMIN FRANKLIN,	JOSEPH MORRIS,
ISRAEL PEMBERTON, jun.	HUGH ROBERTS,
JOHN SMITH,	WILLIAM GRIFFITTS,
SAMUEL RHODES,	ISAAC JONES,
JOHN REYNELL,	EVAN MORGAN.

T R E A S U R E R, CHARLES NORRIS.

T H E Managers re-chofe the following Phyficians and Surgeons to attend the Hofpital for the enfuing Year, *viz.* Doctors *Thomas Bond*, *Phineas Bond*, *Thomas Cadwallader*, *John Redman*, *Samuel Prefton Moore*, and *William Shippen*.

I N the Beginning of 1754, Spinning-wheels were provided by the Managers, for the Employment of fuch of the Women Patients as may be able to ufe them.

I N the *Second Month*, 1754, a Bill lying before the Houfe of Affembly, for re-emitting and continuing the Currency of the Bills of Credit of this Province, and for ftriking a further Sum, the following Propofal was laid before the Houfe, *viz.*

To

To the REPRESENTATIVES *of the Freemen of the Province of* Pennſylvania, *in Gene-ral Aſſembly met.*

' WE the Subſcribers being perſuaded, that the ſame charitable Diſpoſition which
' induced the Houſe of Repreſentatives ſome Time ago to found an Hoſpital
' for the Relief of the Sick Poor, &c. will ſtill incline them to promote all proper
' Meaſures to render ſo laudable an Inſtitution of the moſt extenſive Service, with
' this View we offer to ſign the Paper Bills of Credit propoſed to be iſſued by the
' Law now under Conſideration, and we will contribute ſuch Sums of Money as may
' by Law become due to us for that Service, towards encreaſing the Capital Stock of
' the ſaid Hoſpital, or to be applied in ſuch other Manner, for the Uſes thereof, as
' the Managers may think moſt proper.'

Submitted with all due Reſpect to the Conſideration of the Houſe,

2d Mo. 11th, 1754.		
Hugh Roberts,	Charles Jones,	Joſeph Saunders,
John Reynell,	Samuel Hazard,	George Spofford,
Joſeph Wharton,	Samuel Rhodes,	John Poke,
John Smith,	Joſeph Morris,	Joſeph King,
James Pemberton,	Samuel Sanſom,	Owen Jones,
Iſaac Greenleafe,	Edward Pennington,	Iſrael Pemberton,
Iſaac Jones,	Thomas Clifford,	Jonathan Evans,
Thomas Croſby,	William Grant,	William Logan,
Daniel Williams,	Thomas Say,	Samuel Burge.

AND three of the Members of the Houſe, *viz. Edward Warner, Evan Morgan,*
and *Joſeph Fox,* offered to ſign the ſaid Money upon the ſame Terms, and their
Names were accordingly inſerted in the Bill*.

IN the ſame Month the Accounts of the Hoſpital were laid before the Houſe of
Aſſembly, and a Committee appointed to examine them, and to viſit the Hoſpital,
who having accordingly done ſo, made their Report in Writing, which (having re-
cited the foregoing general State of the ſaid Accounts) concludes thus :

' WE alſo report, that by the Liſt of Patients, we find, that from the Eleventh
' of *Second Month,* 1752, to the Fourth of *Fifth Month,* 1753, there were Sixty-
' four Patients received into the Hoſpital, afflicted with Lunacy, and various other
' Diſorders, which required the Conveniences of ſuch a Place ; of which Number
' Thirty-two were cured and diſcharged, and ſome others received conſiderable Re-
' lief. We likewiſe report, that we have viſited the Hoſpital, and find a conſidera-
' ble Number of diſtemper'd Patients there, who are well taken Care of, and the

E   ' Whole

As the Bill miſcarried, nothing was obtained by this kind Propoſal for the Hoſpital.

Whole appears to us to be under very regular and good Management, and likely to anfwer the original Defign.

All which we fubmit to the Houfe,

JOSEPH TROTTER,
WILLIAM CALLENDER,
MAHLON KIRKBRIDE,
GEORGE ASHBRIDGE,

JAMES WRIGHT,
JOHN ARMSTRONG,
MOSES STARR.

ABOUT this Time a Seal was procured by the Managers; it was engraven on Silver, the Device, the good *Samaritan* taking the fick Man, and delivering him to the Inn-keeper, with thefe Words underneath, *Take Care of him, and I will repay thee.*

THE Twenty-feventh of *Fourth Month,* 1754, *John Reynell,* and *John Smith,* the Committee appointed for that Purpofe, reported an Account of Patients remaining on the Twenty-eighth of *Fourth Month,* 1753, and of fuch as have been admitted into the *Pennfylvania* Hofpital from that Time to the Twenty-feventh of *Fourth Month,* 1754, from which it appears that there were Sixty-one Patients.

Of which 28 were cured and difcharged.
- 7 received confiderable Benefit.
- 2 difcharged at the Requeft of their Friends.
- 1 difcharged for Difobedience to Rules.
- 2 judg'd incurable.
- 5 died.
- 16 remained.

In all, 61

AND the Committee appointed to ftate and fettle the Accounts to this Time, made their Report, of which the following is an Abftract.

On a general State of the Accounts, it appears that

Dr. *The Stock granted by Act of Affembly for building, founding, and furnifhing* Cr.
the Hofpital.

TO Cafh lent out on Land Securities in the Treafurer's Hands, £ 1850 0 0	By Cafh of the Truftees of the Loan-Office, at two Payments, - - £ 2000 0 0	
To Expences of Furniture, Houfe-rent, &c. adjufted 4th of 5th Mo. 1752, - - - 143 5 7½	By Intereft received by the Treafurer laft Year, - £ 67 0 0	
Ditto, 5th of 5th Mo. 1753, 42 4 9½	Ditto this Year, - 160 0 0	
Ditto, 6th of 5th Mo. 1754, 84 12 7	227 7 0	
£ 2120 3 0	£ 2227 0 0	
Ballance due to the Stock, 106 17 0		
£ 2227 0 0		

Dr.

Dr.	*The Capital Stock of the* Pennsylvania *Hospital.*	Cr.

To Fifty-seven Bonds remaining due from sundry Subscribers, amounting to	£ 1389 16 8	By One Hundred and Thirty-three Subscriptions before the Settlement of Accounts, on the 4th of 5th Mo. 1752,	£ 2721 16 8
To Twenty-three Subscriptions for which Bonds are not yet given,	198 0 0	By two additional Subscriptions in 1753,	30 0 0
To Land Securities in the Treasurer's Hands, for Money lent to Persons on Interest,	1000 0 0	By one Ditto, in 1754,	10 0 0
To Deeds in the Treasurer's Hands for a Lot near *Germantown,* and an Annuity of *Thirty-five Shillings Sterling per Annum,* both which were valued at	74 0 0		£ 2761 16 8
	£ 2661 16 8		
Ballance in the Treasurer's Hands,	100 0 0		
	£ 2761 16 8		

Dr.	*The Houshold Expences of the* Pennsylvania *Hospital.*	Cr.

To Ballance of last Year's Account,	£ 97 0 11¾	By Interest-money received from the Subscribers,	£ 140 4 9
To the Amount of Provisions, Firewood and Wages, from the 4th of 5th Mo. 1753, to this Day,	326 2 0¾	Received from the Borrowers of Money lent,	57 0 0
	£ 423 3 0½	By Donations from several Charity-Boxes,	1 15 0
		By Cash received for the Boarding of Pay Patients,	53 18 6
			£ 252 18 3
		Ballance expended more than is yet received,	170 4 9½
			£ 423 3 0½

WE likewise find that the Amount of Subscriptions collected from Widows and other charitable Women, towards paying for the Medicines received from *Sylvanus* and *Timothy Bevan* last Year, and paid into the Hands of *William Griffitts,* is *One Hundred* and *Eleven Pounds, Five Shillings* and *Six-pence,* and that the Ballance remaining due on Account of said Medicines, is *Seventy-nine Pounds, Sixteen Shillings* and *Four-pence Halfpenny,* which ought speedily to be discharged.

Submitted to the Board of Managers,

Philadelphia, 6 5th *Mo.* 1754.

HUGH ROBERTS,
ISRAEL PEMBERTON.

AB-

ABSTRACT of Cases admitted into the Pennsylvania Hospital, from the Eleventh of the Second Month, 1752, to the Twenty-seventh of the Fourth Month, 1754.

	Admitted.	Cured.	Relieved.	Irregular Behaviour.	Incurable.	Taken away by their Friends.	Dead.	Remaining.
Agues	3	3						
Cancer,	3	2						1
Colliquative Purging,	2						2	
Consumption,	1					1		
Contusion,	1							1
Cough, of long standing,	1	1						
Dropsies,	9	4	1				3	1
Empyema,	1	1						
Eyes disordered,	2	1	1					
Falling Sickness,	3	1			2			
Fevers,	2	2						
Fistula in *Ano*,	3	2	1					
—— in *Perinæo*,	2	1						1
Flux,	1						1	
Gutta Serena,	1	1						
Hair Lip,	1							1
Hypocondriac Melancholy,	1							1
Hypopyon,	1	1						
Lunacy,	18	2	3		4	6		3
Mortification,	1						1	
Prolapsus *Ani*,	1	1						
—— *Uteri*,	1	1						
Palsy,	1	1						
—— of the Bladder,	1							1
Rheumatism and Sciatica,	6	4						2
Scorbutick and scrophulous Diseases,	9	6	1	1				1
Ulcers, with Caries, &c.	37	21	4	2	1	3	3	3
Vertigo,	1	1						
Uterine Disorder,	1	1						
Wen,	1	1						
Wounded,	1	1						
In all,	117	60	11	3	7	10	10	16

N. B. The Majority of the Lunaticks taken in had been many Years disorder'd, and their Diseases become too habitual to admit of Relief ; others whose Cases were recent, and might probably have been cured, being put in at private Expence, were so hastily taken away by their Friends, that sufficient Time was not allowed for their Recovery : The Managers have therefore, as well for the Sake of the Afflicted, as the Reputation of the Hospital, resolved to admit none hereafter, who are not allowed to remain twelve Months in the House, if not cured sooner, or judged by the Physicians to be incurable.

The Choice of the Sick to be supported on the publick Stock, was confined to such only whose Cases could not be healed properly in their respective Habitations, but required the extraordinary Conveniences and Advantages of an Hospital ; amongst these, several, for want of this noble Charity in Time, had languished too long to receive any other Advantage from it than the Relief of their Poverty, and the Satisfaction of being convinced they had every Chance for Recovery that Care and Tenderness could afford.

FROM

FROM the foregoing Accounts it appears, That from the Tenth of *February*, 1752, to the Twenty-feventh of *April*, 1754, which is but about two Years and two Months, fixty Perfons, afflicted with various Diftempers, have been cured, befides many others that have received confiderable Relief, both In and Out-patients; and if fo much Good has been done by fo fmall a Number of Contributors, how much more then may reafonably be expected from the liberal Aid and Affiftance of the Well-difpofed who hitherto have not join'd in the Undertaking? Experience has more and more convinced all concerned, of the great Ufefulnefs of this Charity.----The careful Attendance afforded to the Sick Poor; the Neatnefs, Cleannefs, and Regularity of Diet with which they are kept in the Hofpital, are found to contribute to their Recovery much fooner than their own Manner of Living at Home, and render the Phyfick they take more effectual. Here they have the beft Advice, and the beft Medicines, which are Helps to Recovery, that many in better Circumftances in different Parts of the Province do not enjoy. In fhort, there is fcarce any one Kind of doing Good, which is not hereby in fome Manner promoted; for not only the Sick are vifited and relieved, but the Stranger is taken in, the Ignorant inftructed, and the Bad reclaimed *; prefent Wants are fupplied, and the future prevented, and (by eafing poor Families of the Burthen of fupporting and curing their Sick) it is alfo the Means of feeding the Hungry, and cloathing the Naked.

IT is therefore hoped, that by additional Benefactions from pious and benevolent Perfons (an Account of which will be publifhed yearly according to Law) this Charity may be farther extended, fo as to embrace with open Arms all the Sick Poor that need the Relief it affords, and that the Managers will not, in Time to come, be under a Neceffity, from the Narrownefs of the Funds, of refufing Admittance to any proper Object. ' It is hoped that a deaf Ear will not be turn'd to the Cries ' of thofe, in whofe Favour both Religion and Humanity ftrongly plead; who are ' recommended by the great Pattern of human Conduct; who in Sicknefs are loft ' to Society; who contribute greatly to the Inftruction of thofe Youth to whom ' the Lives of High and Low may hereafter be entrufted, whofe Prayers are to be ' fent up for their Deliverers; but that all will affift to render the Funds of this ' Hofpital anfwerable to the Neceffities of the Poor.------Incapacity of contributing ' can by none be pleaded; the Rich only indeed can beftow large Sums, but moft ' can fpare fomething yearly, which collected from many, might make a handfome ' Revenue, by which great Numbers of diftrefs'd Objects can be taken Care of, and ' relieved, many of whom may poffibly one Day make a Part of the bleffed Company ' above, when a Cup of cold Water given to them will not be unrewarded. Let ' People but reflect what unneceffary Expences they have been at in any Year for ' vain Superfluities or Entertainments, for mere Amufements or Diverfions, or per- ' haps in vicious Debauches; and then let them put the Queftion to themfelves, ' Whether they do not wifh that Money had been given in the Way now propofed? ' If this Reflection has Influence on their future Conduct, the Poor will be pro- ' vided

* The kind Vifits and Converfation of fome ferious Perfons, and the pious Books that have been left in the Hofpital, recommended to the Perufal of the Patients, together with the exact Regularity, kept in the Houfe, have been attended with a Bleffing in thefe Refpects.

' vided for. The leaft Mite may be here given without a Blufh ; for what People
' would not chufe to give the Treafurer, or any Manager, the Trouble to receive,
' may be put into their Charity-boxes, or into the Box which is fixed in the Entry of
' the Hofpital : Where Money cannot fo well be fpared, Provifion or Linen, Blan-
' kets, and any Kind of Furniture, Herbs and Roots for the Kitchen, or the Apo-
' thecary, or other Neceffaries of a Family, may be delivered to the Matron or Go-
' vernefs ; old Linen, and even Rags, for Lint, Bandages, and other chyrurgical
' Dreffings, are acceptable, being fcarce to be purchas'd fometimes for Money ; and
' tho' they are of little or no Value to thofe who have them, they are abfolutely
' neceffary in fuch an Hofpital, and will be thankfully received.'

I T ought in Juftice to be here obferved, that the Practitioners have not only given their Advice and Attendance *gratis*, but have made their Vifits with even greater
Affiduity and Conftancy than is fometimes ufed to their richer Patients ; and that the
Managers have attended their Monthly Boards, and the Committees the Vifitations
of two Days in every Week, with greater Readinefs and Punctuality than has
been ufually known in any other publick Bufinefs, where Intereft was not immediately concerned ; owing, no Doubt, to that Satisfaction which naturally arifes in
humane Minds from a Confcioufnefs of doing Good, and from the frequent pleafing
Sight of Mifery relieved, Diftrefs removed, grievous Difeafes healed, Health reftored, and thofe who were admitted languifhing, groaning, and almoft defpairing of
Recovery, difcharged found and hearty, with chearful and thankful Countenances,
gratefully acknowledging the Care that has been taken of them, praifing G O D,
and bleffing their Benefactors, who by their bountiful Contributions founded fo excellent an Inftitution.

N. B. *All Perfons who fhall be difpofed to contribute to the Support of this Hofpital*
by Will, are advifed to do it in the following Manner.

Item, *I give and bequeath to the Contributors to the* Pennfylvania *Hofpital, the Sum*
of   to be paid to their Treafurer for the
Time being, and applied towards carrying on the charitable Defign of the faid Hofpital.

Erratum. In Page 10, the fifth Line from the Bottom, for *and when*, read *and where.*

LIST

LIST *of the* CONTRIBUTORS *to the* Pennsylvania HOSPITAL.

A

WILLIAM AL-LEN, *Esq*; £ 150 0 0

Ditto, *per Ann.* during Life, 12 0 0
Stephen Anthony, 10 0 0
John Armitt, - 20 0 0
William Attwood, 50 0 0

B

John *and* James Bankson, 10 0 0
Anthony Benezet, 10 0 0
Daniel Benezet, 15 0 0
William Blair, - 10 0 0
John Blakey, *Hatter*, 1 0 0
John Bleakley, - 50 0 0
Thomas Bond, - - 25 0 0
Phineas Bond, - 10 0 0
John Bowman, - 12 0 0
William Branson, 50 0 0
John Brooks, - 5 0 0

C

Thomas Cadwallader, 25 0 0
John Campbell, - 3 0 0
William Clemm, 3 0 0
John Coates, - 10 0 0
Warwick Coates, - 5 0 0
Joseph Cox, - 5 0 0
Moses Cox, - 3 0 0
Joshua Crosby, - 100 0 0
Thomas Crosby, - 25 0 0

D

David Deshler, - 15 0 0

E

George Emlen, - 100 0 0
Joshua Emlen, - 10 0 0
Samuel Emlen, *junior*, 13 10 0

F

Richard Farmar, 10 0 0
William Fishbourne, 15 0 0
Joshua Fisher, - 10 0 0
Enoch Flower, - 15 0 0
Joseph Fox, - - 25 0 0
Benjamin Franklin, 25 0 0

Solomon Fussell, £ 10 0 0

G

John Goodwin, *junior*, 10 0 0
Thomas Græme, - 20 0 0
William Grant, - - 10 0 0
George Gray, *Brewer*, 15 0 0
Isaac Greenleafe, - 20 0 0
William Griffitts, - 10 0 0

H

David Hall, - 10 0 0
Adam Harker, - 10 0 0
Arent Haffert, - - 25 0 0
Samuel Hazard, - 10 0 0
Edward Hicks, - 10 0 0
Augustine Hicks, - 5 0 0
William Hinton, - 2 0 0
William Hodge, - - 5 0 0
Andrew Hodge, - 4 0 0
Joshua Howell, - 10 0 0
John Hughes, - - 10 0 0
Philip Hulbert, - 5 0 0

J

Abel James, - - 15 0 0
Robert Janney, - 10 0 0
Derrick Johnson, 25 0 0
Joseph Johnson, - 5 0 0
Matthew Johns, - 10 0 0
Isaac Jones, - - 10 0 0
Charles Jones, - 15 0 0
John Jones, *Merchant*, 10 0 0

K

John Kearsley, - 30 0 0
John Kearsley, *junior*, 10 0 0
Joseph King, - 10 0 0
Matthias Koplin, - 24 0 0

L

John Lassell, - - 5 0 0
Thomas Lawrence, *junior*, 10 0 0
Joseph Leech, - 10 0 0
Jacob Lewis, - 10 0 0
Thomas Lightfoot, - 15 0 0
Thomas Livezey, *junior*, 4 0 0

James

L					P				
James Logan,	-	£25	0	0	William Plumsted,	-	£25	0	0
John Lord,	-	5	0	0	John Pole,	-	15	0	0
Joseph Lownes,	-	12	0	0	Samuel Powell,		50	0	0
James Lownes,	-	10	0	0	R				
Benjamin Loxley,	-	12	0	0	Andrew Rambo,	-	5	0	0
M					John Redman,	-	10	0	0
Wight Massey,	-	10	0	0	John Reynell,	-	40	0	0
William Masters,	-	27	0	0	Samuel Rhodes,	-	10	0	0
John Meas,	-	10	0	0	Joseph Richardson, *Merchant*,		15	0	0
Rees Meredith,	-	40	0	0	Francis Richardson,		15	0	0
Jonathan Mifflin,	-	33	6	8	Hugh Roberts,	-	25	0	0
George Mifflin,	-	25	0	0	John Ross,	-	15	0	0
John Mifflin,	-	25	0	0	S				
Samuel Mifflin,	-	25	0	0	Samuel Sansom,	-	15	0	0
William Moode,	-	10	0	0	Thomas Say,	-	10	0	0
Samuel Preston Moore,		30	0	0	Edward Shippen,	-	10	0	0
Robert Moore,	-	25	0	0	William Shippen,	-	10	0	0
Evan Morgan,	-	10	0	0	John Smith,	-	50	0	0
Anthony Morris,	-	75	0	0	Peter Sonmans,	-	12	0	0
Anthony Morris, *junior*,		50	0	0	Christopher Sour,		25	0	0
Joseph Morris,	-	15	0	0	Charles *and* Alexander Stedman,		40	0	0
Samuel Morris, *Sheriff*,		10	0	0	Thomas Stretch,	-	10	0	0
Morris Morris,	-	10	0	0	T				
N					Adam Thomson,	-	10	0	0
Samuel Neave,	-	25	0	0	Joseph Trotter,	-	10	0	0
John Nelson,	-	10	0	0	Robert Tuite,	-	20	0	0
William Nicholson,		3	0	0	U				
John Nixon,	-	10	0	0	John Unbekandt,		10	0	0
Samuel Noble,	-	10	0	0	W				
Isaac Norris,	-	100	0	0	William Wallace,	-	10	0	0
Charles Norris,	-	25	0	0	James West,		3	0	0
Peter Nygh,	-	10	0	0	Joseph Wharton,	-	50	0	0
P					Townsend White,	-	10	0	0
John Palmer,	-	10	0	0	John Wier,	-	5	0	0
Thomas Paschall,	-	10	0	0	Robert Willan,	-	10	0	0
Oswald Peele,	-	25	0	0	Daniel Williams,	-	10	0	0
Israel Pemberton,	-	100	0	0	Caspar Wistar,	-	50	0	0
Israel Pemberton, *junior*,		100	0	0	John Wistar,	-	20	0	0
James Pemberton,	-	25	0	0	Edmund Woolley,	-	5	0	0
John Pemberton,	-	25	0	0	James Wright,	-	20	0	0
Edward Pennington,		20	0	0	Z				
Richard Peters,	-	50	0	0	Lloyd Zachary,	-	30	0	0

The E N D.